Bright Wonders

ECONOMY READING SERIES

Louise Matteoni
Floyd Sucher
Marvin Klein
Karen Welch

THE ECONOMY COMPANY

Oklahoma City
Indianapolis
Los Angeles

Cover Illustration: William Mathison

Permission to use or adapt copyrighted material appearing
in this book is gratefully acknowledged on pages 347-348,
which are hereby made a part of this copyright page.

ISBN 0-8332-2596-0

THE ECONOMY COMPANY, Educational Publishers
1200 Northwest 63rd Street
Oklahoma City, Oklahoma 73116-5712

 2 3 4 5 6 7 8 9 10 — 90 89 88 87 86 85

Contents

Words to Know for Safety

Deciding

Where the Bear Went over the Mountain

Art of the North American Indians

Words to Know for Math

Aesop's Fables ☆

The Library

Seeing

Wondering

Remembering

Imagining
The Wizard of Oz
a play by L. Frank Baum, ☆ adapted by Lynne Sharon Schwartz

UNDERSTANDING

I have
planted two seeds
in the ground, to sprout up,
grow tall, blossom together and
be friends!

Myra Cohn Livingston

11

The Rooster Who Understood Japanese

Yoshiko Uchida

Mr. Lincoln

"Mrs. K.!" Miyo called. "I'm here!"

Every afternoon when Miyo came home from school, where she was in the third grade, she went to the home of her neighbor, Mrs. Kitamura, whom she called "Mrs. K."

This was because Miyo's mother was a doctor at University Hospital and didn't get home until supper time.

It was a fine arrangement all around because Mrs. Kitamura was a widow, and she enjoyed Miyo's company. Not that she was lonely. She had a basset hound named Jefferson, a ten-year-old parrot named Hamilton, a coal black cat named Leonardo, and a pet rooster named Mr. Lincoln. She talked to all of them in Japanese. She also talked to the onions and potatoes she'd planted in her front yard instead of a lawn, coaxing them each day to grow plump and delicious.

About the time Miyo came home from school, Mrs. K. was usually outside talking to her potatoes and onions, but today Mrs. K. was nowhere to be seen. She wasn't out front, and she wasn't in back talking to any of her animals either.

Her dog, Jefferson, stretched sleepily and came to greet Miyo as she opened the gate to the backyard.

"Hello, Jefferson Kitamura," Miyo said. "Where's Mrs. K.?"

Jefferson wagged his tail and sniffed at Miyo. Then he went back to his special spot at the foot of the willow tree and curled up to get on with his afternoon nap.

Miyo stopped next to see Mr. Lincoln. He was strutting about in his pen making roosterlike sounds and looking very intelligent and dignified. Mrs. K. had told Miyo that he understood every word she said to him, whether she spoke in English or Japanese.

"Mrs. Kitamura, *doko?*" Miyo said, asking Mr. Lincoln where she was.

He cocked his head, looked at her with his small bright eyes, and uttered a squawking sound.

Miyo shrugged. Maybe Mr. Lincoln did understand Japanese, but it certainly didn't do her any good if she couldn't understand what he said back to her.

"Never mind," she said. "I'll find her." And she hurried toward the brown shingled house covered with ivy that hung over it like droopy hair. The back door was unlatched, and Miyo walked in.

"Mrs. K., I'm here," she called once more.

Miyo went into the dining room and found Mrs. K. sitting at the big oval table. She was making herself a cup of ceremonial Japanese tea, whipping up the special powdered green tea in a beautiful tea bowl with a small bamboo whisk.

"*Mah!*" Mrs. K. said, looking startled. "I was so busy with my thoughts, I didn't even hear you come in."

Miyo looked at the pale green froth of tea in the tea bowl, knowing it was strong and bitter. "Is that our afternoon tea?" she asked, trying not to look too disappointed.

"No, no, not yours," Mrs. K. answered quickly. "Just mine. I made it to calm myself." She turned the bowl around carefully and drank it in the proper three and a half sips. "There," she sighed.

"Are you calm now?"

Mrs. K. shook her head. "Not really. Actually, not at all. As a matter of fact, I am most upset."

Mrs. Kitamura stood up and started toward the kitchen, and Leonardo appeared from beneath her chair to follow close behind.

Miyo wondered now why Mrs. K. was so upset. Usually she was full of fun, but today she scarcely smiled at Miyo.

"I've been upset since seven o'clock this morning," she explained suddenly.

"Why?" Miyo asked, gratefully accepting a glass of milk. "Did you get out of the wrong side of bed?"

That was what her mother sometimes asked when Miyo was grumpy. But that wasn't Mrs. K.'s trouble at all.

"It's not me. It's my new neighbor, Mr. Wickett. He told me that if Mr. Lincoln didn't stop waking him up by crowing at six in the morning, he was going to report me to the police for disturbing the peace! What am I going to do?" Mrs. K. asked, as though Miyo were the wise old woman in the Japanese tale who could answer any puzzling question put to her.

"I can't go out and tell Mr. Lincoln he is not to crow anymore. You and your mama have never complained."

Miyo didn't say that they were already up at six o'clock anyway. She wondered what she could say to make Mrs. K. feel better, and finally she said, "I'll ask my mother. She'll know what to do."

"Don't worry, Mama will think of something," Miyo said as she left Mrs. Kitamura's house.

When Miyo got home, Mother was just starting supper. "Hi sweetie," she called. "How was Mrs. K.?"

"She was worried," Miyo answered as she began to set the table. "She has to make Mr. Lincoln stop crowing."

"Whatever for?"

Miyo quickly told Mother about Mr. Wickett. "Mr. Lincoln doesn't hurt anybody."

But Mother said, "Well, I can see Mr. Wickett's side too. If I could sleep late, I'm not so sure I'd like having a rooster wake me at six o'clock. Besides," she added, "our town is growing, and we're in the city limits now. Maybe Mrs. K. will just have to give Mr. Lincoln away."

Miyo didn't even want to think of such a thing. "But he's not just any old rooster," she objected.

He certainly wasn't. Mrs. K. had raised him since he was a baby chick, thinking that he was going to become a hen and give her an egg for breakfast every day.

Mother nodded sympathetically. "I know," she said. "Well, maybe we can think of something."

But nobody could. Not Mother, not Miyo, nor Mrs. K.

That first night Mrs. K. brought Mr. Lincoln inside the house and put him into a big cardboard carton in her bedroom.

"Poor Mr. Lincoln," she said to Miyo the next day. "He nearly smothered, and I hardly got any sleep at all. He crowed in the morning anyway, but I don't think Mr. Wickett heard him because so far the police haven't come. But I jump every time my doorbell rings. What on earth are we going to do?" she asked, wrapping Miyo into the bundle of her troubles.

Miyo wished she had an answer, but all she could say was, "Mama and I are both thinking hard."

But Mother was so tired at the end of a long day looking after sick babies and children at the hospital that she just couldn't find any good ideas inside her head. She did say, however, that keeping Mr. Lincoln inside a carton in the house was not the answer.

And Mrs. K. certainly found out it wasn't. On the second night she brought him inside, Mr. Lincoln poked his way right out of the carton and walked all over her house. He scratched the floors and pecked at her sofa and got into a fight with Leonardo, the cat.

"I suppose I will have to give Mr. Lincoln away," Mrs. K. murmured sadly. "But I can't give him to just anybody. It has to be someone who will love him and not turn him into fricassee or stew."

"If I can't find a new home for Mr. Lincoln, I suppose I will simply have to go to jail," she said, trying to look brave.

Miyo thought and thought until her jaws ached. How in the world could they find just the right person to take Mr. Lincoln? Then, suddenly, she had an idea.

"I know," she said brightly. "I'll put an ad in our class magazine."

Mrs. K. thought about it. "Well," she said slowly. "I suppose it won't do any harm."

Answer these questions.

1. What did Mrs. K. say that Mr. Lincoln could do?

2. Why did Mrs. K. make a cup of ceremonial Japanese tea?

3. Why did Miyo want to help Mrs. K. find a home for Mr. Lincoln?

The Rooster Who Understood Japanese

Mr. Botts

Miyo's class magazine was almost ready to be mimeographed for the month of October. There were several sections, one each for news, feature stories, science, sports, book reviews, poetry, and finally, a small section for ads. That's where Miyo thought Mr. Lincoln would fit nicely.

She made her ad very special. She wrote, "WANTED: NICE HOME FOR FRIENDLY, INTELLIGENT, DIGNIFIED ROOSTER. P.S. HE UNDERSTANDS JAPANESE." Then she added, "PLEASE HURRY! URGENT!"

The magazine came out on September 30. That very afternoon, a policeman rang the doorbell of Mrs. K.'s shaggy ivy-covered house.

"I've a complaint, Ma'm," he said, "about a rooster?" He seemed to think there might have been some mistake.

Mrs. K. sighed. "Come inside, officer," she said. "I've been expecting you." She supposed now she would just have to go quietly to jail, but first she wanted a cup of tea. "Would you like some tea?" she asked.

Officer McArdle was tired and his feet hurt.
"Thank you," he said, and he came inside.

"Dozo," she said, "please have some tea." She
took off her apron and smoothed down her frizzy
gray hair. Then she told him all about her
troubles with Mr. Lincoln.

He looked sympathetic, but he said, "You're
breaking a city law by having a rooster in your
yard. You really should be fined, you know."

Mrs. K. was astonished. "Even if I am only
barely inside the city limits?"

Officer McArdle nodded. "I'm afraid so. I'll
give you two more days to get rid of your rooster.
Mr. Wickett says you're disturbing the peace."

Then he thanked her for the tea and he was
gone.

26

Miyo was proud of the ad in her class magazine, but no one seemed at all interested in Mr. Lincoln. Instead, several people told her how much they liked her feature story about Mr. Botts, the school custodian, who was retiring.

She had written, "Say good-bye to the best custodian Hawthorn School ever had. Mr. Botts is retiring because he is getting tired. At the age of sixty-five, who wouldn't? He and Mrs. Botts are going to Far Creek. He is going to eat a lot and sleep a lot and maybe go fishing. So, so long, Mr. Botts. And good luck!"

On her way home, Miyo ran into Mr. Botts himself. He told her it was the first time in his entire life that anyone had written a feature story about him.

When he got home that night, he took off his shoes, sat in his favorite chair, and read the magazine from cover to cover. At the bottom of page twenty, he saw Miyo's ad about Mr. Lincoln.

"Tami," he said to Mrs. Botts, who happened to be Japanese, "how would you like to have a rooster?"

"A what?"

"A rooster," Mr. Botts repeated. "One that understands Japanese."

Mrs. Botts thought that Mr. Botts had had too much excitement, what with his retirement party at school and all. But he kept right on talking.

"When we move to Far Creek, didn't you say you were going to grow vegetables and raise chickens while I go fishing?"

Mrs. Botts remembered having said something like that. "Yes, I guess I did."

"Well, if you're going to raise chickens, you'll need a rooster."

"Why, I guess that's so."

"Then we might as well have one that's friendly and dignified," Mr. Botts said, and he went right to the telephone to call Miyo.

"I'll take that rooster you want to find a home for," he said. "My wife could talk to it in Japanese too."

Miyo couldn't believe it. Someone had actually read her ad and that someone was Mr. Botts. He and his wife would give Mr. Lincoln a fine home and surely wouldn't turn him into fricassee or stew. As soon as she told Mother, she ran right over to tell Mrs. K. the good news.

When Miyo told Mrs. K. that Mr. Lincoln would have a nice half-Japanese home in Far Creek with Mr. and Mrs. Botts, Mrs. K. gave Miyo such a hug she almost squeezed the breath out of her.

"Hooray! *Banzai!*" Mrs. K. said happily. "Tomorrow we will have a party to celebrate. I shall invite you and your mama, and Mr. and Mrs. Botts." And because Mrs. K. felt so relieved and happy, she even decided to invite Mr. Wickett.

"Even though you are a cross old man," she said to him, "I suppose you were right. A rooster shouldn't live in a small pen at the edge of town. He should live in the country where he'll have some hens to talk to and nobody will care if he crows at the sun."

Mr. Wickett was a little embarrassed to come to Mrs. K.'s party, but he was too lonely to say no. He came and said, "I'm sorry I caused such a commotion."

But Mrs. K. told him he needn't be sorry. "Life needs a little stirring up now and then," she admitted. "Besides," she added, "now both Mr. Lincoln and I have found new friends."

"You come on out to visit us and your rooster any time you like," Mr. Botts said.

Miyo's mother promised that one day soon she would drive them all up to Far Creek to see how Mr. Lincoln liked his new home.

When the party was over, Mr. Botts carried Mr. Lincoln in a crate to his station wagon. Mr. Lincoln gave a polite squawk of farewell and Mrs. K. promised she would come visit him soon.

"Good-bye, Mr. Lincoln. Good-bye, Mr. and Mrs. Botts," Miyo called.

"I hope we'll see each other again soon," Mr. Wickett said to Mrs. K.

"Good night, Mr. Wickett," she answered. "I'm sure we will."

Miyo and her mother thanked Mrs. K. for the nice party and went home, leaving her to say good night to her potatoes and onions before going inside.

"Do you think she'll miss Mr. Lincoln a lot?" Miyo asked.

"She will for a while," Mother answered, "but now she has a new friend and neighbor to talk to."

Miyo nodded. That was true. And even if Mr. Wickett couldn't understand Japanese, at least he could answer back, and maybe that was even better than having an intelligent rooster around.

Miyo was glad everything had turned out so well, and went to bed feeling good inside.

"Good night, Mama," she called softly to her mother.

"Good night, Miyo," Mother answered as she tucked her in.

Then, one by one, the lights went out in all the houses along the street, and soon only the sounds of the insects filled the dark night air.

Answer these questions.

1. Why did Miyo write a feature story about Mr. Botts?

2. What was Mrs. Botts going to do when they moved to Far Creek?

3. Why did Mrs. K. have a party?

4. Why was Mr. Wickett embarrassed to go to Mrs. K.'s party?

About the Author

Yoshiko Uchida, who grew up in Berkeley, California, has written many books about Japan, its children, and Japanese-Americans. She wants her readers to understand that although people around the world have different customs, they share similar joys.

Words
in Our
Hands

Ada B. Litchfield

My name is Michael Turner, and I am nine years old. I have two sisters, Gina and Diane, a dog named Polly, and two parents who cannot hear me when I talk.

They never have heard me, because my mom and dad were born deaf.

My parents never heard any sounds at all when they were babies. Some people think a person who can't hear can't learn to talk, but that's not true.

My mom and dad went to a school for deaf kids when they were growing up—that's where they were taught to talk. They learned by placing their fingers on their teacher's throat and feeling how words *felt* in her voice box as she said them. They learned how words *looked* by watching her lips and face as she spoke. It's hard to learn to say words that way, but my parents did.

Sometimes my mother and father can understand what people are saying by reading their lips. That's another thing my parents learned at their school—lip reading.

How we move our bodies and what our faces look like when we talk help our parents read our lips, but most of the time we talk to them with our hands as well as our mouths. My Grandma Ellis says we have words in our hands.

My mother and father learned sign language when they were little. And they taught us signs when we were babies, just as hearing parents teach their children words. Our grandparents, friends, and neighbors helped us learn to talk.

My parents have some neat things to help them. In our house, when the telephone or doorbell rings, flashing lights come on. We have a TTY—a teletypewriter—attached to our phone. The teletypewriter spells out messages on tape, and then my parents can type messages back.

Of course, the person calling us has to have a teletypewriter, and not very many people do. That means that many times we kids have to talk on the phone for our parents. And sometimes we have to talk to people who come to the door.

When we were babies, my mother or father checked on us very often to be sure we were all right. They took turns at night. They also used a cry alarm, which is a microphone hooked up to a light. When we cried, a light would flash in our parents' bedroom or in the kitchen or living room.

When Diane was little, Gina and I helped take care of her. We would hear when she cried and tell my mom or dad.

Some deaf people have a hearing-ear dog to help them, and we have Polly. Polly hasn't been taught hand signals the way real hearing-ear dogs have, but she is learning to do many things a hearing-ear dog does.

Polly gets my mother up by tugging at her blankets if her flashing-light alarm doesn't wake her. She runs back and forth to let my mom and dad know that someone is at the door. She makes a big fuss if a flashing-light alarm goes off or if a pan is boiling over on the stove.

Just because my parents are deaf doesn't mean we don't do things other families do. My mom and dad go to programs at school. We have friends over for dinner and to stay all night. We go on picnics, and sometimes we drive to the city to the Science Museum.

We are a happy family—at least we were until about six months ago. Then the publishing company where my father has always worked moved to a new town, one hundred miles away.

My father is an editor of a magazine about farming. Nobody in the family wanted to move, but my father loves his job so, of course, he wanted to move with his company.

We bought a new house with a big yard that everybody liked, but it took a long time to get used to our new town. Before, my mom had always done all the shopping and banking for our family. Now she felt a little strange going into a store where the people didn't know her, so very often she wanted Gina or me to go with her.

In our old town, everybody was friendly and knew our family. Nobody stared when they saw us talking with our hands. But in the new town, people did stare, and sometimes Gina and I felt embarrassed.

Gina and I didn't want to feel that way, and we understood how shy our parents felt. We knew Mom missed her art class. We knew they both missed their old friends and were as lonesome and homesick as we were!

One day Gina's favorite teacher gave her a note to take home. It was an invitation for our family to go to a performance of the National Theatre of the Deaf.

At first, I didn't want to give the invitation to my parents. I didn't want them to go because I didn't want people to make fun of them or feel sorry for Gina and me.

But Gina said they should go. She said that the play would be in sign language, and who would understand it better than our parents? I knew she was right, and besides, Mom and Dad needed to go out and meet new people.

Still, I was worried about what might happen. The night of the play, all sorts of questions were popping into my mind as I dragged myself up the steps into the hall.

The theatre was filled with people. Just inside the door, my mother signed to me, "Where will we sit?"

To our surprise, a man stood up and said, "There are five seats over here."

We couldn't believe it—he was talking in sign language!

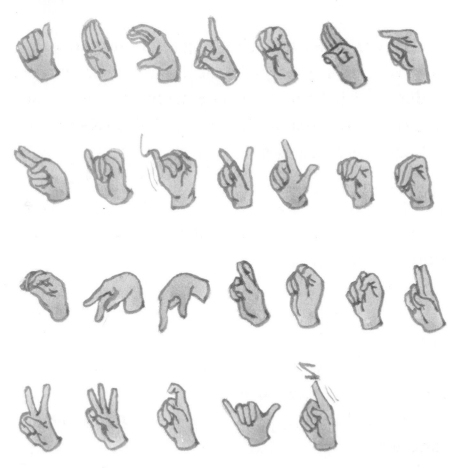

All around us, people were laughing and talking. They seemed so friendly. Many of them were talking with their hands, and they didn't seem to care who was watching.

Before the play started, we learned from our program that some of the actors were deaf and some could hear. The hearing actors and some of the deaf actors would speak in the play. All of the actors would sign, sometimes for themselves and sometimes for each other, and sometimes they would all sign together. Everyone in the audience would be able to understand what was going on.

The play we saw was called *The Wooden Boy*, and it was about Pinocchio, a puppet who wanted to be a real boy.

After the play, we went backstage to meet the actors. The deaf performers talked with people who knew sign language. The hearing actors helped the other people understand what was being said.

I was proud of my parents. They were smiling, and their fingers were flying as fast as anyone's. For the first time in many months, they seemed to feel at home.

Then we had another surprise when Gina's teacher came over to us. She talked very slowly and carefully so my mother could read her lips; then she signed with her hands!

Gina was excited, because her favorite teacher, who wasn't deaf, had words in her hands, too. Gina was learning something she didn't know before; we all were. We were learning there were many friendly people in our new town who could talk with our parents. I decided this place wasn't going to be so bad after all.

Answer these questions.

1. How did Michael's parents learn to talk, to read lips, and to use sign language?

2. Why does Grandma Ellis say that the members of Michael's family have words in their hands?

3. How does the dog, Polly, get Michael's mother up in the morning if the flashing-light alarm does not wake her?

4. How would Michael's mother feel about doing the shopping and banking in the new town after meeting people at the play?

Words to Know at a Drugstore

Do you ever shop in a drugstore? The items below can be found in a drugstore.

Toothbrush   Powder
Toothpaste   Shampoo
Plastic bandage   Cotton balls
Tissues   Skin lotion

These items can also be found in other stores. Name other kinds of stores where you have seen these items.

Number your paper from 1 to 7. Write the words from the list that make the sentences correct.

1. I clean my teeth with a _____ and _____.

2. Do you use _____ to wash your hair?

3. You will need _____ when you have a cold.

4. I used _____ to put medicine on my knee.

5. I put a _____ over a scratch on my knee.

6. _____ helps dry skin feel softer.

7. We use baby _____ on our baby.

Home-run Hannibal

Robert D. Culp

The baseball left the pitcher's hand and streaked toward Hannibal. It reached the plate chest high, a perfect pitch.

Hannibal's swing was perfect, too. The bat connected solidly, and he watched the ball arch high over the left fielder's head and drop beyond the ball park fence.

Hannibal heard the cheers of his teammates as he loped around the bases. *My first homer as a Mustang,* he thought. *Look at the fellows waiting at home plate. If this doesn't make me one of the team, nothing will.*

He had been with the team for only a week, so it was natural that he wouldn't be a leader. Hannibal understood that, but he couldn't understand why he was frozen out of their everyday fun. Now perhaps that would change.

Hannibal came up to bat one more time and struck out on three mighty swings. The game ended. The Mustangs had lost again, 4–2. Hannibal's home run hadn't been enough.

The Mustangs played six games over the next two weeks, but they won only two. Hannibal played well in right field. He caught eleven flies and he even made one difficult, diving catch.

At bat, Hannibal had a harder time. He swung as hard as he could when the pitch came near the plate. True, he got two more home runs, but he struck out fourteen times.

Each time Hannibal hit a homer he thought everything was going to be all right at last. The Mustangs crowded around and clapped him on the back. Each time Hannibal was again convinced that if he hit the homers, the team would accept him.

The next game was against the top team in the league, the Rockets. The Mustangs had not beaten this team yet during the season, and a loss would push the Mustangs into last place.

After practice the day before the game with the Rockets, Hannibal found himself walking home silently beside Bernie. Bernie tried to talk baseball with Hannibal, until finally Hannibal spoke up.

"I'm trying my best, Bernie. Don't the others know that?"

Bernie looked startled. "Nobody's mad at you, Hannibal. Some of the kids get mad when you go for homers all the time, but most of them know you just aren't much of a hitter."

Now Hannibal was surprised. "I can hit. I've hit three home runs," said Hannibal, "and I'll get more. Just wait."

"I guess that's the trouble," said Bernie slowly. "You seem to be more interested in your home runs than in the team, Hannibal."

The Mustangs played well against the Rockets. The game went one way and then the other. When the bottom half of the final inning came, however, the Mustangs trailed by two runs. It was their last chance.

The Mustangs came through. Two singles and a double tied the score, 6–6. The next Mustang hit a long fly ball into right field for the first out, but the runner on second advanced to third after the catch. The next batter struck out. Two out—one more chance.

Hannibal was up next. Bernie whispered, "Remember, just a single, Hannibal, and you can win it for us."

Hannibal didn't reply, but as he faced the pitcher he thought, *I can hit a homer easier than I can hit a single. I may not be much of a hitter, but I've got three homers. This will be my fourth.*

Hannibal took a mighty swing at the first pitch. The ball fouled up over the backstop. A groan came from the Mustang dugout.

Hannibal saw Bernie's pained expression and didn't see the next pitch flash by. Strike two.

"A single, Hannibal," pleaded Bernie. "Just a single."

Hannibal watched the Rocket pitcher uncertainly. He looked at their infielders playing far back, confident that all they needed was one out. Hannibal made his decision.

The pitch came. Hannibal gritted his teeth and squared around. He met the ball with a motionless bat and laid down a perfect bunt.

The ball rolled down the third base line. The runner at third hesitated a moment, and then he raced for home. It was a perfect play.

The Mustangs had won, 7–6. Hannibal felt himself covered by a swarm of cheering teammates. He looked around and smiled. He was right in the middle of the team.

Answer these questions.

1. What did Hannibal think he had to do to be accepted by the team?

2. What did Bernie say that Hannibal was more interested in?

3. Why were the Rocket infielders playing far back when Hannibal came up to bat?

4. When Hannibal was up to bat against the Rockets, what did he decide to do?

Write on your own.

Near the end of the game Hannibal bunted the ball. He made the decision in favor of the team. Write six sentences telling what might have happened if he had hit a homer instead.

Associations

Home to me is not a house
Filled with family faces;
Home is where I slide in free
By rounding all the bases.

A tie to me is not
Clothing like a hat;
It means the game is even up
and I wish I were at bat.

Eve Merriam

Pettranella

Betty Waterton

Long ago in a country far away lived a little girl named Pettranella.

One dark winter night, Pettranella's father came home with a letter.

"It's from Uncle Gus in America," began her father. "He has his homestead there now, and is already clearing his land. Someday it will be a large farm growing many crops of grain."

When he had finished reading the letter aloud,
Pettranella said, "I wish we could go there, too, and
live on a homestead."

Her parents looked at each other, their eyes
twinkling with a secret. "We *are* going," said her
mother. "We are sailing on the very next ship."

Pettranella could hardly believe her ears.
"Grandmother," cried Pettranella, "now you will
have a real flower garden, not just a window
box."

Pulling her close, her grandmother said gently,
"But I cannot go to the new land with you, little one.
I am too old to make such a long journey."

Pettranella's eyes filled with tears.

When they were ready to leave, her grandmother gave her a small muslin bag. Pettranella opened it and peered inside. "There are seeds in here!" she exclaimed.

"There's a garden in there," said her grandmother. "Those are flower seeds to plant when you arrive at your new home."

"Oh, I will take such good care of them," promised Pettranella, "and plant them in a beautiful garden for you."

So they left their homeland.

At last they reached the shores of Canada. Then they travelled up a wide river and across the lonely land.

After many days they came to a settlement, where they camped. Then they bought some things they would need: an axe and a saw, a hammer and nails, sacks of food and seed, a plow and a cow and a strong brown ox, and a cart with two large wooden wheels.

The ox was hitched to the cart, which was full of all their belongings.

One day as they followed the narrow winding trail through groves of spruce and poplar, there was a sudden THUMP, CRACK, CRASH!

"What happened?" cried Pettranella.

"We have broken a shaft," said her father, "because one of the wheels went over a big rock."

They began to unload the cart. "We'll make a new shaft," said her father; and, taking his axe, he went into the woods to cut a pole that would fit.

Pettranella helped her mother fix lunch, then sat down on a log to wait. Taking the bag of seeds from her pocket, she poured them out into a little pile on her lap, thinking all the while of the garden she would soon be making.

Just then she heard a familiar creaking and squeaking, and it was getting closer.

"Somebody's coming!" she shouted, jumping up.

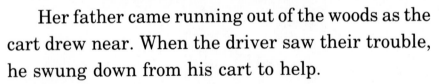

Her father came running out of the woods as the cart drew near. When the driver saw their trouble, he swung down from his cart to help.

He helped her father make a new shaft, then they fastened it in place and loaded the cart again.

Afterwards they all had lunch and talked together. Their new friend said that he had a homestead nearby and he invited them to visit one day.

"Do you have any children?" asked Pettranella.

"A little girl just like you," he laughed, as he climbed into his cart. Pettranella waved good-bye as he drove off. "Our neighbor says it isn't far now," said her father.

As they bumped along the trail, suddenly Pettranella thought about the flower seeds. She felt in her pocket, but there was nothing there. The muslin bag was gone!

"Oh, oh! Stop!" she cried. "The seeds are gone!"

Her father halted the ox. "I saw you looking at them before lunch," said her mother. "You must have spilled them there."

"I'm going back to look," said Pettranella.

She found the log, but she didn't find any seeds. Just the empty muslin bag.

As she trudged back to the cart, her tears began to fall. "I was going to make such a lovely garden, and now I broke my promise to Grandmother!"

"Maybe you can make a vegetable garden instead," suggested her mother, but Pettranella knew it wouldn't be the same.

It was later that afternoon when they found their homestead.

The next morning her father began to put up a
small cabin. Then he started to break the land. A
small piece of ground was set aside for vegetables,
and after it was dug, it was Pettranella's job to rake
the soil and gather the stones into a pile.

"Now we can plant the garden," said her
mother, and they did.

A few days later when Pettranella looked, she
saw rows of tiny green shoots.

If only I hadn't lost Grandmother's seeds, she
thought, flowers would be sprouting now, too.

One warm Sunday a few weeks later, Pettranella went to help her father hitch up the ox, for this was the day they were going to visit their neighbors.

The ox cart bumped and bounced down the narrow trail over which they had travelled so many weeks before.

Suddenly her father stopped the cart and jumped down. "There's the rock where we broke the shaft," he said. "This time I will lead the ox around it."

"And there's the log I was sitting on when I lost the seeds," said Pettranella. "And look! LOOK AT ALL THOSE FLOWERS!"

There they were, blowing gently in the breeze, their bright faces turned to the sun— Grandmother's flowers.

"Oh," cried Pettranella, "I've never seen such beautiful flowers!"

"You can plant them beside our house," said her father, "and make a flower garden there for us to enjoy."

Pettranella did, and she tended it carefully, and so her promise to her grandmother was not broken after all.

But she left some of the flowers to grow beside the trail, that other settlers might see them and not feel lonely.

Answer these questions.

1. Where were Pettranella and her family going to live?

2. How did Pettranella lose the seeds that her grandmother had given her?

3. In what season of the year did Pettranella and her family arrive at their homestead?

4. Why did Pettranella leave some flowers to grow beside the trail?

Words to Know for Safety

Have you seen any of the signs below? These signs help keep you safe. It is important to be able to read these signs and understand what they mean.

Caution

Pedestrian crossing

Private property

Railroad crossing

No diving

Explosives

High voltage

First Aid

Number your paper from 1 to 8. Read each of these sentences. Write the words from the sign beside the number of the sentence it matches.

1. Do not go into this building or yard without asking.

   _____

2. The water here is shallow or has very dangerous rocks. _____

3. Do not touch any wires or machinery near this sign.

   _____

4. People may cross at this place. _____

5. These are very dangerous and might blow up. _____

6. You must be very careful. _____

7. You can get help here if you are hurt. _____

8. Look carefully for trains before you cross. _____

Vocabulary Review

Read each sentence and the four answers that follow it. Decide which answer best completes the sentence. Write the answer on your paper.

1. An arrangement is a _____ that is made.
   a. delay
   b. plot
   c. plan
   d. square

2. To make a complaint is to tell what is _____.
   a. wrong
   b. right
   c. changed
   d. dark

3. The audience is the _____ who watch the play.
   a. visitors
   b. tourists
   c. people
   d. performers

4. To be confident is to be _____.
   a. useful
   b. controlled
   c. wrong
   d. sure

5. Shoots are new _____ in the garden.
   a. rocks
   b. plants
   c. fences
   d. seeds

Books to Read

Brown, Marion Marsh and Ruth Crone *The Silent Storm*

 This book is a biography of Anne Sullivan, the teacher of the blind, deaf, and mute Helen Keller.

Carroll, Ruth Robinson and Latrobe *Tough Enough*

 Tough Enough is a mischievous dog who is blamed for doing some destructive things until he leads Beanie, his Aunt, and Beanie's sister to higher ground during a flash flood. The dog then becomes a hero.

Cleary, Beverly *Ramona and Her Mother*

 Ramona's mother goes to work and her home life goes through some changes. Ramona decides to run away from home, but as her mother helps her pack, Ramona discovers some things about herself.

Luce, Willard and Celia Luce *Lou Gehrig: Iron Man of Baseball*

 Lou Gehrig was a famous baseball player. This biography of his life emphasizes his enthusiasm for baseball, his devotion to his family, and his determination to do his best in everything.

DECIDING

I'll sail my boat to-morrow
  In wonderful new places,
But first I'll take my watering-pot
  And wash the pansies' faces.

Amelia Josephine Burr

71

Where the Bear Went over the Mountain

Blaine G. Goodman

As Judy reached for the matches above the stone fireplace of the log cabin where she and her family had just moved, a letter fluttered to the floor. Her brother Stan got to it first and said, "I want the German stamp."

"O.K.," said Judy, "but what's written in the letter?"

Stan removed some yellow paper from the envelope and read the letter out loud:

Dear Jim,

When I first came to Germany, I did not intend to stay, but I've changed my mind. I concealed all the Indian artifacts in the cave where I found them, and I put the artifacts from the gold-rush days with them. Thought they'd be safe there until you moved into the cabin.

Now, if you intend to open a store, the artifacts are all yours, or if not, just leave them. If someone can locate the cave "where the bear went over the mountain," well, finders keepers.

Yours, Bill

"I'd really enjoy having those gold-rush things, if we can find them," Stan remarked.

"But that was years ago," said Judy. "I bet that man Jim found them."

"Maybe," said Stan, "but we could look."

"But how do we find 'where the bear went over the mountain'?" asked Judy.

"I don't know," said Stan, "but possibly Dad can examine the letter and help us."

They showed the letter to their father; however, he just put the letter back into the envelope and shook his head, remarking, "This isn't bear country, so I don't know what this letter means."

Stan and Judy thought Mr. Curry would possibly know about Jim and the cave, so they went to search for him. In a few minutes they were in the old man's log cabin, waiting anxiously for his opinion. After he'd read the letter, he said, "Although your dad is right, in my opinion the story is true, and I remember Jim. He talked about opening a store, but one day he just left, and I never saw him again."

"Maybe we ought to begin searching for a cave," said Judy.

"Before you do," said Mr. Curry, "would you bring me some firewood? There's a pile of logs up the road, and you can fill your sacks with them."

Judy and Stan went to the firewood pile and began to fill the sacks. The sun was setting when Judy glanced up from her work.

Suddenly she shouted, "Look!"

"What's the matter?" asked Stan.

Judy pointed to a cluster of low mountains. When Stan looked, his eyes got big with surprise.

One of the low mountains had some unusual rocks on it and, as the sun set, it cast a shadow against another, larger mountain. The shadow looked like it was moving over the larger mountain.

"It looks like—a bear!" Stan shouted.

"What do you know about that!" said Judy.

"It's our bear," Stan said, "and tomorrow morning we ought to hike up the mountain and locate that cave. We'll know right where to search for it."

Both children arose early the next morning and dressed rapidly. They hiked up the low mountain toward the unusual rocks. When they finally reached the rock that had cast the shadow of the bear, Stan shook his head, saying, "Although this is the place, it doesn't look as if there's a cave around here."

Judy moved aside some bushes and crawled around a big rock. When she was safe on the other side, she pushed aside the rock, which hurtled down the mountain.

She suddenly pointed to where the rock had been and said, "It concealed the opening of the cave."

They both peered excitedly into the cave, and Stan shouted, "There it is!" He pointed at two big black boxes.

Stan and Judy dragged the boxes from the cave, and then they dragged them home.

They opened the boxes and found the Indian and gold-rush artifacts Bill had written about. At the bottom of one box Judy found a small leather bag and asked, "What's this?"

Stan glanced up and said, "That's a leather bag made to hold gold nuggets."

Judy examined the bag, turned it over, and poured several rust-brown rocks into her hand. Gold spots dotted the rocks. "They're gold nuggets!" shouted Judy.

"And to think," Stan said, "we didn't know if we'd enjoy being here on the mountain."

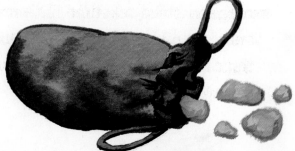

Answer these questions.

1. What had Bill concealed in the cave?

2. What did Judy notice while she was gathering firewood?

3. What did Judy find at the bottom of one of the black boxes?

4. Why did Stan and Judy think they wouldn't enjoy being on the mountain?

Write on your own.

    Judy and Stan gave the artifacts and the gold nuggets to the museum. The museum director asked them to write a short description of how they discovered the artifacts. Pretend you are Judy or Stan and write the description.

Art of the North American Indians

Shirley Petersen

Many beautiful forms of art have come to us from the North American Indians. Much of that art tells a story. What materials the Indians used to tell stories usually depended on the materials available in the area where they lived.

Indians of the Northwest

In the northwest part of our country, there were many huge trees. So the Indians who lived there made good use of this wood. They made boats, bowls, and cooking utensils from the wood. They also used the wood from the giant red cedar to carve totem poles.

The Northwest Indians used totem poles to tell stories in much the same way people today use pictures in books. The different characters in the story, or legend, were carved into the totem pole. Each different figure stood for an important event in the story. The storyteller would "read" the story from top to bottom by recalling the events shown by each figure.

Men's robes were painted with pictures that showed brave deeds. Tepees were painted with designs that were supposed to protect the owners from bad times. Each family had its own special design, which could not be copied.

The Plains Indians made their paints with roots, plants, and bark. The paint was put on with a stick or a sharp bone.

Indians of the Plains

The Plains Indians also told stories and recorded important events with their art. Unlike the Northwest Indians, they didn't have many trees, but they did have plenty of buffaloes.

The Plains Indians moved around, following the buffalo herds. Buffaloes provided the Plains Indians with meat for food, hides for tepees and clothes, bones for tools, and horns for containers. Nothing was wasted.

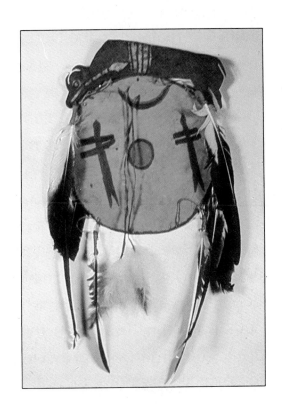

79

Plains Indians were also famous for their beadwork. Beads were used to decorate clothes, moccasins, carrying pouches, and cradles.

Indians of the Woodlands

The Indians who lived on the East Coast and in the midwest part of this country are known as Woodland Indians. Although trees were plentiful, the Woodland Indians used them differently than the Northwest Indians did.

Woodland Indians carved faces on trees, but they didn't make them into totem poles. Instead they used them as masks. These masks were often painted and decorated with feathers. Woodland Indians also made masks from dried corn husks because corn could be grown easily in this area. These masks were used for special ceremonies.

To tell stories or record important events, the Woodland Indians made wampum belts. These were long pieces of cloth with pictures woven into them with wampum beads. Wampum beads were usually made from different kinds of shells.

The Woodland Indians were the first people to use quillwork. The quills of porcupines were dropped into boiling dyes made from berries. Then they were woven together to form a design, or they were sewn directly into the cloth. Quillwork spread to other American Indian groups. It soon became a fine art used to create many beautiful designs.

Indians of the Southwest

The Southwest Indians did not have the trees or the buffaloes that other American Indian groups had. But they did have lots of grazing land and clay.

The Southwest Indians became famous for their woven blankets and rugs. They raised goats and sheep for their wool. They made yarn from this wool and dyed it different colors. The yarn was woven on large looms into blankets and rugs with beautiful designs.

Pottery making was another important art of the Southwest Indians. They cut out a round clay bottom and then rolled clay into snakelike shapes called coils. The coils were then stacked one on top of another until the desired size and shape were reached. Sometimes the Indian potters left the coils as they were. Other times, they smoothed out the surface and carved or painted designs on it. Pottery for special ceremonies was sometimes shaped into animal figures.

Today, many examples of North American Indian art can be found in museums. Many people collect Indian art, also. Many American Indian groups still make these forms of art so that the art of their people will not be forgotten.

Answer these questions.

1. How did the Northwest Indians use totem poles?

2. What did the Indians of the Plains paint on men's robes?

3. What did the Woodland Indians make from dried corn husks?

4. Why did the Indians of the Southwest raise sheep and goats?

5. Why did the Indians decorate many of the items that they used every day?

Words to Know for Math

Do you sometimes see words in your math book you don't know? These are important math words. They will help you understand math better.

Measure   Divide

Triangle   Fraction

Multiply   Sum

Metric system Meter

Number your paper from 1 to 8. Choose the best word to complete each sentence. Write the words on your paper.

1. A part of a whole is called a _____.
   cube   meter   fraction
2. The answer to an addition problem is the _____.
   triangle   meter   sum
3. A figure that has three sides is a _____.
   length   triangle   fraction
4. To take one number times another number is
   to _____.
   measure   multiply   divide
5. To find out how many times one number will go into
   another number is to _____.
   divide   add   measure
6. The way to find out the size of something is to _____.
   subtract   add   measure
7. A way that people can weigh and measure things is
   the _____.
   sum   triangle   metric system
8. A metric measure for length is a _____.
   fraction   meter   inch

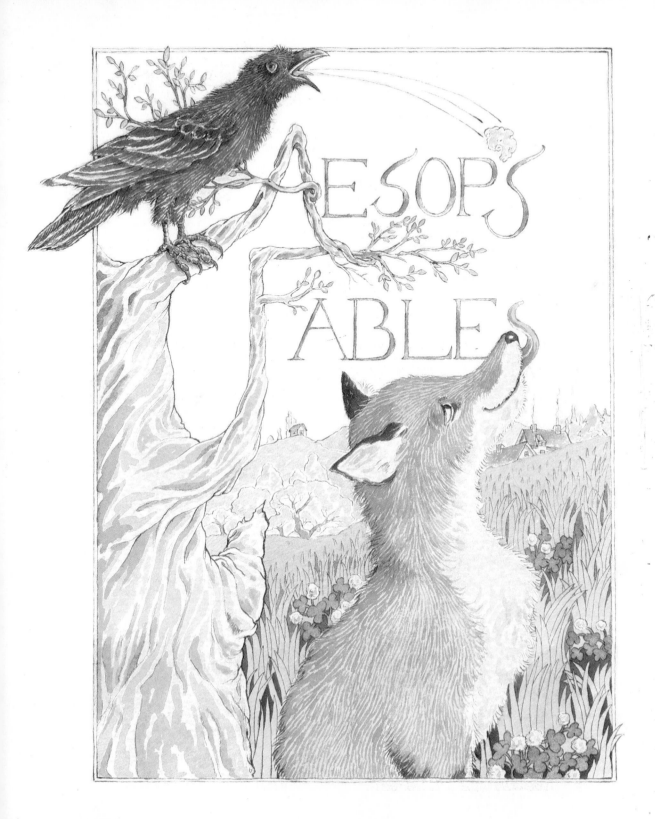

AESOP'S FABLES

THE fox AND THE Crow

A crow snatched a piece of cheese from a window. She flew with it to a tree, where she could enjoy eating it. A fox saw her as she was enjoying the cheese. He came and stood beneath the branch on which she sat.

"O crow," he said, "what beautiful wings you have! What bright eyes! What a graceful neck you have! Your feathers are as beautiful as the eagle's! Surely your voice must equal your beauty. Please sing to me and let me hear for myself."

The crow, pleased with the compliments the fox had given her, opened her mouth to give a caw—and down fell the cheese!

The fox snapped up the cheese and walked away.

Beware of flatterers.

THE WIND AND THE SUN

An argument once arose between the north wind and the sun as to which of them was the more powerful.

They could not agree. So they decided to have a contest. They looked down on the road below them. A traveler was passing by. They decided to try to make him take off his coat.

The north wind started the contest. He sent a strong cold blast to try to blow the traveler's coat away. But instead of taking off his coat, the man hugged it to his body more closely than ever.

The sun laughed at the failure of the north wind. Then with all his power, he drove the thick, watery clouds from the sky. Then he spread his warmth upon the head of the weather-beaten traveler.

The man became so hot that he was unable to endure it any longer. So he first took off his coat. Then he sat in the shade of some trees which grew near the road.

Persuasion is better than force.

Answer these questions.

1. What did the crow snatch from the window?

2. What did the fox mean when he said that the crow's voice must equal her beauty?

3. What did the north wind and the sun decide to do to settle their argument?

4. What did the traveler do when the sun began to shine on him?

The Library

It looks like any building
When you pass it on the street,
Made of stone and glass and marble,
Made of iron and concrete.

But once inside you can ride
A camel or a train,
Visit Rome, Siam, or Nome,
Feel a hurricane,
Meet a king, learn to sing,
How to bake a pie,
Go to sea, plant a tree,
Find how airplanes fly,
Train a horse, and of course
Have all the dogs you'd like,
See the moon, a sandy dune,
Or catch a whopping pike.
Everything that books can bring
You'll find inside those walls.
A world is there for you to share
When adventure calls.

You cannot tell its magic
By the way the building looks,
But there's wonderment within it,
The wonderment of books.

Barbara A. Huff

The Skates of Uncle Richard

Carol Fenner

Marsha

Nine-year-old Marsha dreamed about a beautiful, tall, slender ice-skating champion who could leap high into the air and spin very fast.

Marsha, in real life, had been watching the championship skaters on television since she was six. She had never skated on real ice skates, but often she would pretend to skate when she was alone in her room. But pretend skating was not the same as dreaming of being the beautiful ice-skating champion that she imagined.

The days grew shorter and shorter. Then one day it snowed. Winter was really on its way, and thoughts of her birthday came into Marsha's dreaming head. She began to hint to her mother that she sure would like ice skates for her birthday this year.

"When you can watch where you're walking, and when you can wipe the silverware without dropping it," her mother said, "maybe then you can handle ice skates."

Marsha had never had a good reason before to watch where she walked or to keep hold of the silverware, because she had more exciting things on her mind. But even if she tried hard to be more alert, Marsha didn't think she would ever get ice skates for her birthday.

Marsha worried about what would happen to the beautiful skater in her head if the real Marsha ever got real ice skates on her real feet. Her dream skating, her leaps and spins, might not come true at all.

After a while, whenever Marsha brought up the subject of ice skates, her mother would look sort of thoughtful. Marsha's hopes rose, but her worry about losing the dream skater who lived in her head rose, too.

Now her birthday was here. Marsha's eyes flew over the packages to a large box covered with red tissue. It had silver stars pasted into the shape of her initial, a big starry *M*. Her heart crowded into her throat.

She couldn't bring herself to open the red box right away. First she unwrapped a new dress with a lace collar, and two new books. But her mind was on the box covered with red tissue. She grew first hot, then cold, from excitement.

She opened a paint set. Her older brother, Leonard, gave her a flashlight. Finally the present covered with red tissue was the only one left to open.

She tore at the tissue, careful not to rip into the big *M*. The box inside looked like the one her last year's winter boots had come in. When she opened it up, there inside the whispering tissue bulged the ugliest ice skates she had ever seen.

For a while, Marsha just sat staring at the skates. Then she took them out of the box. They were old-fashioned hockey skates, not in the least the kind of skates a figure skater would wear.

"They were your uncle Richard's skates," said her mother, "when he was seven. He was about your size then. He kept them up real nice so they're almost good as new."

Marsha kept her eyes on the skates. Uncle Richard was old now . . . old, at least thirty. She could feel tears pushing to get out from behind her eyes.

"Your uncle Richard is a fine skater," her mother continued. "He learned how to skate on those skates. They'll be a good start for you, Marsha, till we see how you take to skating."

Marsha sat on the floor with the ugly skates in her lap. "I remembered packing them away in the attic years ago," her mother was saying. "Richard'll be pleased to know they're being used," she added tartly, ". . . if he ever stops by long enough for a little conversation."

But Marsha was feeling the beautiful skating champion inside her head disappear. Her dream had deserted her and the ugliest skates in the world lay in her lap.

Answer these questions.

1. What did Marsha dream about?

2. What did she want for her birthday?

3. Why did Marsha wait to open the red box?

4. Why did Marsha's mother give her Uncle Richard's old skates instead of new skates?

The Skates
of Uncle Richard

Uncle Richard

One Saturday, several weeks after her birthday, Leonard agreed to take Marsha skating at the lagoon. Marsha had stuffed the skates in the back of her closet. She took them out. They fit, but her ankles wobbled. Maybe it would be different on the ice.

But it wasn't different. She kept falling down. It wasn't fun and her ankles began to ache. Finally, Leonard pulled her across the ice to a bench and went to skate with his friends.

Marsha sat on the bench, alone and miserable. She wanted to go home, but she didn't know how she would ever get back across the frozen lagoon.

Suddenly, a man was standing in front of her, smiling. She saw he was leaning toward her, saying something, and she recognized her uncle Richard.

He was saying, "Marsha, why are you looking so sad?" Marsha didn't know how to tell him, so she changed the subject. "Momma's mad at you again," she said shyly, "because you haven't been by."

"Your momma is always mad at me," said Uncle Richard. "I was out of town," he added absently. Marsha saw he was studying her skates. "Why don't you lace up your skates properly?" he asked. As he bent way over and touched them thoughtfully, Marsha could see he was puzzled.

"They were your first skates when you were seven," she explained in a low voice. Uncle Richard knelt down in front of her and took one of her feet in both of his hands. "Yeah," he whispered, "they sure are." He looked up at her with delight growing in his face. "Those good old skates." He laughed and then he began to undo the laces. "First off, Marsha, you've got to have your skates laced properly."

Uncle Richard laced the skates very tightly and evenly across her foot and above her ankle.

Then he stood her up and began to pull her slowly and evenly across the ice. "Bend your knees, not your middle," he told her. When she did so, she was surprised at how easily she could balance.

After they had gone a short distance, Uncle Richard said, "You do that real easy, so I want to show you some things to practice here while I get some skating done." First he showed Marsha how to rest her ankles whenever they got tired. "Stand quietly. Breathe easy. Let your feet go soft."

Then he said, "Here's something else to practice." He pushed forward into one foot and trailed the other behind lightly without touching the ice. "Just bend your knee and lean into it," he said, "nice and easy.

"Now you practice that for a while." Marsha nodded and Uncle Richard skated off. She watched to see if he really could skate as well as her mother said.

Marsha saw him reach into his pocket and pull out a tiny radio. He held it next to his ear and began to skate to music no one else could hear. Marsha noticed he glided a long time on one foot before he shifted his weight to the other one.

His speed quickened, then he circled into a spin that blurred his entire outline.

"Oh," breathed Marsha, "he is really fine."

Suddenly he swooped and leapt into a single axel. He circled to a halt and began to skate backward, disappearing around a bend in the little island.

Alone in the middle of the ice, Marsha felt her ankles begin to wobble with worry. She tried resting them the way Uncle Richard had taught her and they stopped wobbling. "But I can't stand here forever," she thought. She tested herself, lifting first one foot and then the other.

Then she took a deep breath, bent her knee, and pushed off into her right foot the way Uncle Richard had done. She glided a little, her body balanced over her skating foot. Then she shifted and pushed into her left foot and glided a shaky distance. It worked! Push, glide . . . push, glide. It was fun!

Suddenly she realized she was at the other end of the lagoon. "My, my," said a voice behind her. "I thought I left you down at the other end." It was Uncle Richard. "How'd you get here?" he asked.

"I push-push-glided all by myself till I got here," said Marsha.

"You're one surprising young lady," said Uncle Richard. "You sure learn fast." He bent down and looked seriously into her face.

Marsha felt, in that moment, that Uncle Richard could see inside her heart better than anyone. The beautiful champion figure skater of her dreams floated briefly into her mind, but Marsha didn't have time for her now.

"I want to learn how to skate like you skate," she said. Uncle Richard touched her cheek softly with his fingertips. He looked very thoughtful for a minute, then he said quietly, "Okay, we'll work on it. But you'll have to set your mind to it."

Marsha nodded again. She understood.

Uncle Richard suddenly laughed out loud. "We'll surprise your momma," he said. "Next week we'll have another lesson. I'll talk to your momma and maybe she won't be mad at me."

Marsha beamed at him.

"They're a good old pair of skates. Oil the runners, you hear?" Marsha nodded.

Uncle Richard pushed off. Marsha pushed off after him and glided away on the skates of Uncle Richard, taller and taller and taller, never once falling down.

Answer these questions.

1. Who did Marsha meet while she was sitting on the bench?

2. What three things about skating did Uncle Richard show Marsha?

3. What did it mean that Marsha felt Uncle Richard could see inside her heart?

Write on your own.

Marsha continued to take skating lessons from Uncle Richard. On her next birthday her mother gave her a brand-new pair of figure skates. Marsha insisted her mother go with her to the lagoon to watch her try out the new skates. Write five sentences describing what Marsha had learned in a year.

Hold Fast Your Dreams

Hold fast your dreams!
Within your heart
Keep one still, secret spot
Where dreams may go,
And sheltered so,
May thrive and grow—
Where doubt and fear are not.
Oh, keep a place apart
Within your heart,
For little dreams to go.

Louise Driscoll

Words to Know to Write Letters

Do you like to get letters in the mail? Do you like to get invitations asking you to come to a party? These are some words that you might see in letters or invitations.

Dear	Sincerely
Please	Thank you
P.S.	R.S.V.P.

Choose the best word to put in each space in these notes. Write the invitation and letter on your paper.

_____ come to a birthday party:

When: October 6
Where: Sue's house

_____ 742-4329

_____ Jane,

_____ for the nice game you gave me for my birthday. I love it!

_____,

Ellen

_____ See you soon!

Vocabulary Review

Read each sentence and the four answers that follow it. Decide which answer best completes the sentence. Write the answer on your paper.

1. When something is concealed, it is _____.
   - a. outside
   - b. hidden
   - c. valuable
   - d. contained

2. Pottery is bowls and dishes made from _____.
   - a. wood
   - b. plastic
   - c. clay
   - d. metal

3. An argument between people is a _____.
   - a. disagreement
   - b. secret
   - c. discussion
   - d. ceremony

4. Something that is old-fashioned was used many _____ ago.
   - a. days
   - b. minutes
   - c. months
   - d. years

5. To balance is to keep from _____.
   - a. falling
   - b. beginning
   - c. measuring
   - d. failing

Books to Read

Carlson, Natalie Savage   *A Pet for the Orphelines*

Twenty girls who live in an orphanage near Paris, France decide that they need a pet. Trying to choose one pet for twenty girls becomes an amusing challenge.

Greenfield, Eloise   *Daydreamers*

Illustrated by award-winning artist Tom Feelings, this poem is about children who daydream. It explains that although daydreamers seem to be sleeping, they are actually thinking and growing all the time.

Selden, George   *The Cricket in Times Square*

Chester is a cricket who comes to New York City from Connecticut in a picnic basket. He meets new friends and has wonderful adventures.

Sobol, Donald J.   *Encyclopedia Brown Takes the Case*

Idaville's police chief, Chief Brown, has a secret weapon against crime. It is his son, Encyclopedia Brown. In this book, Encyclopedia solves ten mysterious cases.

SEEING

To look at any thing,
If you would know that thing,
You must look at it long

John Moffitt

115

The Horse Who Went Fishing

Jean Morris

On the hill above the lake, the farmer and his horse were plowing back and forth across the bumpy field under the warm summer sun.

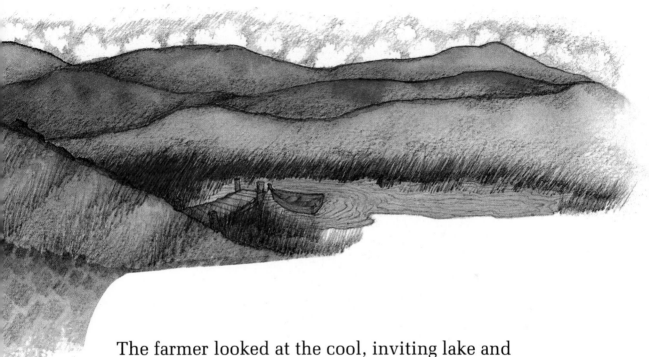

The farmer looked at the cool, inviting lake and thought about fishing.

"Work, work, nothing but work," said the disgusted farmer, looking down at his brightly painted rowboat, tied to the dock. "I really would like to go fishing, but naturally work comes first."

"On the other hand," said the farmer, looking at the shimmering lake, "there is definitely more than one kind of work. I plant seeds for food, and planting is work, so if fish is food, then fishing must certainly be work—and work comes first!"

"It will surely be cool on the lake," the farmer said, "and fried fish will definitely taste good for supper."

The tired horse looked up; he knew what supper was, but what was that about fishing? "I've never gone fishing," he said to himself, "and that rowboat looks too small for two, but I will surely have to go fishing if fishing is work because the farmer has never done any work without me."

The farmer led the horse to the lush meadow, then he hurried up to the house.

"I'm going fishing," he said to his wife.

"What about your lunch?" asked his wife.

"I can eat in the boat," said the eager farmer, "while I work."

"What about your afternoon nap?" asked his concerned wife.

"I can nap in the boat," said the farmer, "while I work."

"What about the baking sun?" asked his wife.

"My hat has a very wide brim," the farmer said thoughtfully.

"You certainly have no bait," said his wife.

"There are millions of snails in the garden," the farmer responded, "and they're eating up your lovely flowers."

"I shall pack you a nourishing lunch at once," said his wife.

The farmer went out and filled a pail with snails.

"Don't forget your lunch," reminded his wife. "Try to take a nap, and definitely wear your hat, and get rid of the snails, and—"

The impatient farmer took his sack lunch and his big-brimmed hat and the pail full of snails and hurried along the winding path past the meadow and down the hill to the lake.

"The good farmer wants me to rest; how kind of him," said the horse, as he watched the farmer go by.

"But it's terribly hot in the meadow, and I'm tired of eating grass. Fish might taste good for supper. I'd better hurry," said the horse as he leaped over the fence and galloped down the hill onto the slippery dock.

"The farmer is a kind man, but he can't do his work without me."

The farmer was already in the little fishing boat, stowing away his gear, and he didn't look up.

"The farmer will surely be glad to see me," said the horse as his foot slipped, and he slid off the end of the dock—SPLASH!

Waves rocked the little red rowboat.

"Who is rocking my boat?" said the farmer angrily as he turned, and into the water he went—SPLASH!

The shivering farmer bobbed to the surface and reached for the side of his rowboat, but the boat was not there.

"Who took my boat?" he said, wiping his eyes and looking around. "I see a small red boat out there, but it isn't mine because there's a horse sitting in it."

"Wait a minute!" he said, looking again. "It's not only my boat, it's also my horse! How could this happen to me; how could this happen to me?"

The boat drifted far out toward the middle of the lake.

"Come back!" the farmer shouted; "come back, back, back!"

The horse heard the farmer shouting and perked his ears.

"Sack, did he say 'sack'?" said the horse to himself as he looked around and saw the sack of lunch the farmer's wife had prepared.

"The farmer wants me to eat his lunch; how kind of him," the horse said, waving at the farmer to show he understood, and he took a big green pickle from the sack.

The boat drifted farther and farther away.

"Swim!" the farmer shouted. "You crazy horse; swim, swim, swim!"

"Brim," said the horse; "did he say 'brim'?" and he looked around and found the big hat.

"The farmer surely wants me to wear his hat; how kind of him," said the horse, and waved to show that he understood and put on the hat at once.

The farmer shouted as the boat drifted farther, "Jump, jump, jump!"

"Dump," said the horse; "did he say 'dump'?" and he looked around and found the pail of snails.

"The farmer wants me to have more room; how kind of him," said the horse, and waved to show that he understood and dumped the snails into the water, pail and all.

"You are a fool, you crazy horse!" the farmer shouted. "And so am I; no horse, no boat, no fish, no pail, no lunch, no hat, no anything. We are fools, fools, fools!" he cried, as he shook his fist at the horse and made his way back to shore.

"The farmer has decided not to fish so he waved good-by, and he hopes I am cool; how kind of him," said the horse. "I shall fish for both of us."

The horse took a bite of the pickle and said, "I hope fish taste better than this." He leaned back in the boat and shut his eyes, and the hat slid over his nose, and the boat drifted on.

"If this is really fishing," said the horse, "I wonder where the fish are?"

He didn't have long to wait, for the boat soon drifted into the reeds and stopped. *Splash*—a fine, shiny fish leaped high out of the water and stared at the horse.

"Well, have you never seen a horse before?" said the horse, sitting up.

"Certainly not eating pickles in a rowboat!" the fish said, so surprised that he promptly flopped into the boat and lay there gasping.

Splash—another fine fish leaped out of the water to stare at the horse.

"Have you never seen a horse before?"

"Not eating pickles and wearing a hat!" said the fish, dropping into the boat and flopping about.

When the horse saw the farmer swimming toward him with a rope he said, "How kind of him; he knows I'm tired of fishing."

The farmer tied the rope to the boat, and then he saw the fish. So he shut his eyes and when he opened them, the fish were still there. The farmer towed the boat to shore, led the horse back to the meadow, and took the fish up to the house.

"How wet and angry you look!" remarked his wife. "Fishing surely must be work, but did you get rid of all the snails?"

"No," said the grumpy farmer, "the horse did."

"That is no way to talk; you are angry because you're hungry and tired," said his wife. "Did you eat your lunch and take a nap in the boat?"

"No," said the farmer, "the horse ate my lunch and took my nap."

"The warm sun has made you angry," his wife said; "and did you wear your hat in the boat?"

"No," said the farmer, "the horse wore my hat in the boat."

"You are angry," said his wife, "but it doesn't matter since you caught two fine fish for our supper—and don't tell me the horse caught the fish!"

"But he did," said the farmer, "so I guess I just can't do my work without him."

Answer these questions.

1. Why did the horse think he would have to go fishing?

2. What time of day did the farmer decide to go fishing?

3. What did the farmer see out in the lake?

4. Who did the farmer say had eaten his lunch and taken his nap?

5. What did the farmer say he could not do without the horse?

Horses in America

Ken Tanaka

Horses Then and Now

Horses have been important to this country ever since they were brought here nearly 400 years ago by the Spaniards. For a long time horses provided the only transportation that many people had. Horses carried people and their belongings from place to place, and they were also used to move farm machines and to herd cattle.

Today transportation is provided by cars, trucks, trains, and planes, and modern farm machines are hauled by tractors. Although some ranchers still use horses in their work, most people ride horses just for fun.

Kinds of Horses

Horses are grouped by size, and the three groups are heavy horses, light horses, and ponies. Heavy horses, with their large bones and strong muscles, can weigh as much as 2,400 pounds. Most light horses have much smaller bones and muscles, and they weigh less than 1,300 pounds. Ponies are horses under five feet tall, and they weigh less than 800 pounds.

Long ago, knights rode heavy horses into battle. Today most heavy horses, such as the Clydesdale, are used only for pulling special wagons or for riding in shows.

Light horses, which have always been used for carrying people and small loads, are the most popular kind of horse today. The quarter horse is one kind of light horse.

Ponies, such as the Shetland, are short and plump. They are good for pulling small wagons and carrying young riders.

Colors of Horses

A horse's body has a fine coat of shiny hair. Horses' coats come in many colors, such as black, brown, red brown, gray, and gold. Some horses have spots on their coats.

There are special names for the white markings on a horse's face. A large patch is a blaze, a small jagged patch is a star, a narrow band down the middle is a race, and a patch near the horse's mouth is a snip.

How to Ride a Horse

If you want to learn how to ride a horse, the best way is to take riding lessons. But always make sure that the horse you are going to mount, or get on, is very gentle.

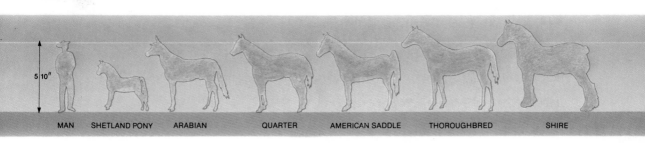

5 10"

MAN   SHETLAND PONY   ARABIAN   QUARTER   AMERICAN SADDLE   THOROUGHBRED   SHIRE

Here are some other things to remember: (1) Always mount from the left side. (2) To mount the horse, put your left foot into the stirrup and swing your right leg over the horse's back. (3) Sit straight, but not stiff, in the saddle. (4) To make the horse go, press your legs against its sides. (5) To stop the horse, pull gently on the reins and lean back. (6) Use the reins and your legs to guide the horse. (7) To guide the horse to the right, press your left leg against the horse's side and pull the reins to the right. (8) To guide the horse to the left, press your right leg against the horse's side and pull the reins to the left.

Caring for a Horse

If you are planning to get a horse, you should know that taking care of it will be an important job. The horse must have plenty of room to run, and it will need its own stall in a barn.

You should provide your horse with a large stall so that it can turn around and lie down. Cover the floor of the stall with straw or sawdust and clean it every day.

Just like a person, a horse needs to eat three times a day. To keep your horse healthy, feed it hay, grass, and oats, and see that it has plenty of fresh water to drink. Give a little bit of salt to your horse each day, because salt keeps it from losing too much water when it sweats.

Take your horse from its stall and exercise it every day. Your horse should also have its coat groomed each day to keep it looking healthy and clean. A well-groomed horse has had its coat, mane, and tail carefully brushed. After it has been groomed, a horse likes to be rubbed down with a soft cloth. Check your horse's shoes often to be sure that nothing is stuck in them, and remember to replace the shoes when they start to wear down.

Horses are beautiful animals, and they can be a lot of fun, but they need very special love and care.

Answer these questions.

1. Why were horses so important to people years ago?

2. What are horses used for today?

3. Why do horses need to be exercised every day?

4. Why should horses be groomed every day?

Motor Cars

From a city window, 'way up high,
I like to watch the cars go by.
They look like burnished beetles, black,
That leave a little muddy track
Behind them as they slowly crawl.
Sometimes they do not move at all
But huddle close with hum and drone
As though they feared to be alone.
They grope their way through fog and night
With the golden feelers of their light.

Rowena Bennett

Words to Know in Magazines

Do you like to read magazines? Here are some special words you may see in magazines.

Photographs   Stories
Illustrated by   Fiction
Table of contents   Articles
Jokes and riddles   Features

Make a list of your favorite magazines and give one reason why each is a favorite.

Number your paper from 1 to 7. Write the word from the list that best tells about each sentence.

1. These would probably make you laugh. _____

2. This tells who drew a picture. _____

3. This lists the parts of the magazine and their pages. _____

4. A camera was used to take this. _____

5. This is a story that someone made up. _____

6. These are special articles or stories. _____

7. These are usually short and give information on a special topic. _____

134

Lost in the Storm

Carol Carrick

It was a windy day in October. Christopher and his dog, Bodger, waited in the ferry shack to keep warm.

When Christopher looked out the window, he could see his friend Gray waiting for him on the other side of the channel. Gray lived on the island just off the shore from Christopher's town. No other family lived there during the winter.

"Guess you're the only one who wants to go across this afternoon," said the ferry operator. He walked with Christopher up the ramp of the two-car ferry. A few seagulls were standing silently on the dock.

"Today's no day for the beach," the old man said. "Even the birds know enough to stay in town."

"I'm going over to play with Gray this afternoon," Christopher explained. He had just moved from the city, and Gray was the first friend he had made in his new school.

The man steered the tiny ferry into the channel. The water was dark and choppy, with white curls of foam.

"Wind is from the east," shouted the man over the whine of the engine. "It's going to make a really high tide."

As soon as they reached the island, Gray grabbed Christopher by the arm. "Come on, let's play before it starts raining."

They righted an overturned rowboat that had been pulled onshore.

Christopher said, "Let's pretend we've landed on this island and we're going to bury our treasure."

Bodger trotted off into the dunes while the boys collected things left by the tide. They discovered a broken picnic basket and filled it with bottles and shells. Their treasure chest grew so heavy with the treasure they had collected that they had to drag it.

The clouds were darkening when the boys heard Bodger's hunting bark. Far down the beach they saw his reddish coat in the tall grass. The wind blew sand in their faces and rolled balls of dried seaweed along the beach.

"Look! I can lie down on the wind!" shouted Chris, leaning into it.

139

They dug a deep hole with their hands and dropped in the basket. Gray picked up a dead crab and chased Christopher with it.

"Put it on top of the chest," called Christopher from a safe distance. "It can guard the treasure."

Gray erected a driftwood board to mark the spot where the treasure was buried.

Suddenly rain was falling in big drops. The boys ran toward Gray's house, shrieking and laughing.

Gray's father was on the porch looking for them, and his troubled look turned into a smile when he saw the boys coming.

"The tide's too high for the ferry to dock," he told Chris. "I called your mother to tell her you would have to stay overnight."

Christopher and Gray danced with delight. They whirled around hugging each other and fell into a heap, giggling.

Then, for the first time, Christopher realized that Bodger hadn't come home with them.

The beach was hidden by the drops that glittered on the porch screen and the sheets of water that spilled from the roof's gutters. Overhead, the pounding rain drowned out the sound of Christopher's voice as he called the dog's name.

Christopher wanted to go looking for Bodger, but Gray's parents wouldn't let him.

"You won't be able to find each other in this storm."

"He'll take care of himself."

"Dogs are smart, you know."

They were both talking at once, trying to convince him.

Gray was silent and his eyes looked troubled. Christopher knew that Gray would have gone out with him if he could. Christopher's own eyes filled with tears.

Gray's father put an arm around each of them and said, "Since you guys are already wet, bring in some wood and we'll build a fire."

The boys each carried in an armload of logs from the woodpile. Then Gray's mother hustled them into Gray's room to dry off and change their clothes.

Hamburgers were just going into the frying pan for supper when the lights went out. Everybody gave a shout of surprise.

"The wind must have blown down an electric line," Gray's father said. "Let's do all we can before dark in case the power stays out all night."

They collected candles, a kerosene lantern, and extra blankets. After that was done, Gray's mother kept them busy. They watched the hamburgers grilling in the fireplace and warmed the buns on the hearth.

The hamburgers were so delicious, and the little house so full of warmth and fun, that Christopher almost forgot about Bodger. But never for very long.

The fire made their faces hot and their eyelids feel heavy. Gray fell asleep on the floor. His mother put him on the couch and covered him. She made a cozy bed for Christopher near the fire by pushing two armchairs together.

Christopher lay listening as the wind blew gusts of rain against the windows and whined around the corners of the house. It sounded like the whimper of a dog. He thought about Bodger, wet and hungry.

Several times he crept to the window to look and listen. But there was only the storm outside. Once he fell asleep and dreamed he had found Bodger.

Daylight came as the storm ended. Christopher woke Gray and they quietly left for the beach.

"It will be easier if we walk along the water where the sand is packed down," Gray suggested.

The water had risen high over the beach. The shoreline was so changed that the boys couldn't even find where the treasure was buried.

Then they saw the dog tracks.

"They must be fresh!" yelled Gray. "Last night's tracks would be washed away."

The paw prints ran along the high water mark for a while, then wandered inland where they disappeared. The boys stood on a high dune and looked in all directions. Nothing moved but water and grass.

They continued to walk along the shore. After a while, the tracks reappeared, but there was still no dog in sight.

"Look!" shouted Christopher. A flight of stairs had been washed up on the beach. Under it they saw Bodger, lying with his head resting on his paws. He lifted it as he heard their voices. The dog galloped toward them, then thundered past. He swerved and returned, jumped on Christopher, and knocked him over. When Christopher tried to grab him he pulled away, tearing around Chris in giddy circles, kicking up the sand with his hind legs. And then he was happily all over Christopher, digging his wet nose in his neck.

When they got home, Gray's mother was fixing breakfast. "The power must have come on while we were sleeping," she said.

She stroked Bodger's head. "See, I told you he could take care of himself." But she looked very pleased nevertheless.

She gave the dog a bowl of milk with two raw eggs in it. Bodger drank greedily, splashing the floor.

When it was time to go home, Gray went down to the dock with Christopher. Gulls were gliding in the cloudless sky, and some were picking over stranded shellfish that had washed up onto the dock.

Gray rang the ship's bell to call the ferry operator over. Christopher was the only passenger again, but he could see cars lining up on the town side to cross for a day of fishing or beachcombing.

"Hey," the old man called, "you're going the wrong way again. Today is beach weather."

"Bodger and I had enough beach," said Christopher sleepily. "We're going home."

About the Author

Carol Carrick has written many books for children. Many of her books are about outdoor adventures. She was born in Long Island, New York. She now lives in Edgartown, Massachusetts. She is the mother of two sons. Her husband, Donald, is an artist who illustrates her books.

Answer these questions.

1. Why were Christopher and Bodger going to the island?

2. Why did the boys stop playing and run to Gray's house?

3. Why were Gray's parents trying to convince Christopher that Bodger would be fine?

4. Where did Christopher find Bodger?

150

Summer Snow

An evening by the sea
just before night
the fishing pier turned
a feathery white,
a lovely white, just as though
all those gulls
were summer snow.

Charlotte Zolotow

Marie Curie

Michael Reynolds

Long ago in Poland, there lived a girl named Manya, who laughed and sang with her three sisters and a brother. Manya's father was a teacher and her mother a musician. Although they encouraged all their children to do excellent schoolwork, nobody could know then just how famous little Manya would grow up to be.

Manya studied hard in her school and became a teacher of poor children in Poland. But Manya was curious about many things, and she wanted to learn more. She went to a famous school in France, the Sorbonne, to learn how and why things do what they do. It was her ambition to be a scientist, at a time when few women were encouraged to study.

While in Paris, Manya began spelling her name as they do in France—Marie. Marie met another energetic young scientist, whose name was Pierre Curie. Both Pierre and Marie were devoted to science, and they found they had a great love for each other as well, so they were married.

Some scientists had just discovered some mysterious new rays called x-rays. This news made Pierre and Marie very curious. It was not known what could be done with the x-rays, so one day Marie told Pierre, "I'd like to discover the secret of these strange rays."

To carry out her ambition, Marie first had to find a laboratory, a place where she could work. Pierre and Marie were poor, and to find the secrets of these rays would take a lot of money.

A school encouraged Marie by giving her a room for her laboratory. It was a gloomy, wet room, but it would do for Marie, and she began to work.

Marie was looking for the secrets of an element that had been found in the ground. It was slow work, and time plodded by, but the dedicated young scientist was getting closer and closer to an important discovery.

Pierre realized this and encouraged her in her work, and together they studied in the laboratory for many months. They finally discovered the element that was the secret of the rays, and they named the element *radium*. But they still couldn't find out exactly what the mysterious element radium looked like.

It was very important work the two scientists were doing, but they had little money to go on. It was cold in the laboratory, and the place would fill with bad gases. Marie's hands had sores and burns, and Pierre became ill. They didn't know then that radium can be harmful. It can make people ill and can even kill them.

After four years Marie and Pierre discovered the secret they had set out to learn. On a dark evening in 1902, Marie and Pierre stood in their laboratory and saw a blue glow of light coming from their radium. It was there before them. They had found the mysterious secret of the radium rays at last! This was an important discovery for the world.

News reporters were at their door, and all kinds of people wanted to see them—scientists, doctors, teachers, and kings. The Curies were very famous now, and they were given the great prize for science, the Nobel Prize. Marie was the first woman to win this prize. The Curies were encouraged in their work by more gifts of money.

The two scientists wanted to get back to their laboratory to begin new work, but by this time Pierre and Marie had an energetic family who kept them busy but happy.

Then during a rainstorm in 1906, Pierre Curie was killed in a terrible street accident. Marie was discouraged because she was now alone, with a family and important work still before her. She went back to the laboratory and began again. The work was even harder than before, but Marie made still more discoveries about radioactivity. One thing she learned was that these rays had hurt her greatly. Her hands were no better. They still had the mysterious sores and burns on them.

In 1911 the Nobel Prize came to Marie once more, making her famous as the first person to win the prize twice.

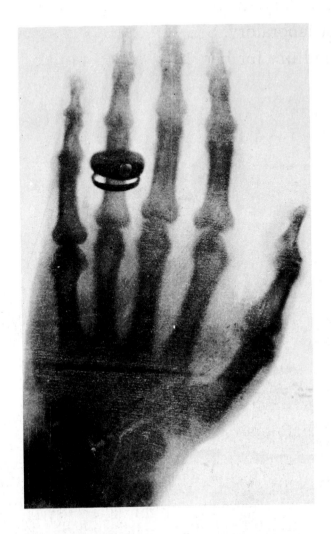

Not long after that, war came, and the energetic scientist wanted to help the wounded. By then doctors knew how to use the deadly source in a good way, to look into the body, so Marie had an x-ray machine made that could be taken to where wounded men were. Marie herself made a lot of trips with the x-ray machine, which helped save many lives.

At last the war came to an end, and Marie went once more to her laboratory. She had to have more of the element radium for her work, but it would cost much money.

When some women in America heard of her new ambition, they encouraged her with a gift of radium. To get the radium, Marie made a trip to America, where she met the president and many famous scientists and teachers.

When she went back to France, she found that everyone wanted to see her. Marie tried to see them all because she was very kind, but it was in her laboratory that she felt best, happy in her work.

In 1934, Marie became quite ill and had to stop her work. The doctors couldn't find out why Marie was so ill, and she became worse and died.

Later, scientists discovered that it was radium that put an end to Marie Curie's life. Marie didn't know that working around radium for many years could make her ill and cause death.

Thanks to Marie and her important discovery, now doctors study the body with x-ray pictures and help ill and injured people more.

Marie gave people another important discovery, as well. Up to that time many people didn't think that women could be scientists, but Marie Curie changed the way they felt. She was a dedicated scientist and a great woman.

Answer these questions.

1. What did Marie want to find out about x-rays?
2. Why did Marie and Pierre want to see what radium looked like?
3. What prize did Pierre and Marie Curie win?
4. Why did Marie have to stop her work in 1934?
5. To what use did doctors put Marie's discovery?

Write on your own.

Pretend you are a mouse that lives in the Curies' laboratory. Describe what you saw the evening that Marie and Pierre discovered the secret of radium.

Words to Know for Social Studies

We have to read from many different kinds of books at school. Our Social Studies books tell us about people and places. These are words from our Social Studies books.

Globe   Ecology
Map   Country
Population   Climate
Laws   Geography

Number your paper from 1 to 8. Read each sentence. Choose the best word from the list of social studies words to match each sentence. Write your answers on your paper.

1. The number of people who live in a place.

2. The rules that the people in a country live by.

3. The study of how living things and their surroundings act on each other.

4. The kind of weather that a certain place has.

5. People who live in the same area and have the same laws.

6. The study of the earth and its life.

7. A drawing that shows roads, streets, states, or countries.

8. A round ball on which is drawn a map of the earth.

Vocabulary Review

Read each sentence and the four answers that follow it. Decide which answer best completes the sentence. Write the answer on your paper.

1. A meadow is a _____ where cows and horses graze.
   a. forest
   b. field
   c. machine
   d. creek

2. To mount something is to get _____ it.
   a. behind
   b. beside
   c. off
   d. on

3. A whimper is a soft, sad _____ that a dog makes.
   a. sound
   b. bark
   c. whistle
   d. growl

4. To have ambition is to want to be _____.
   a. healthy
   b. simple
   c. successful
   d. fun

5. A laboratory is a _____ for doing scientific experiments.
   a. closet
   b. laundry
   c. book
   d. room

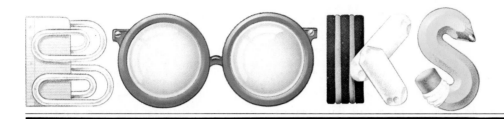

Books to Read

Buehr, Walter   *Storm Warning*

Scientists have developed some effective storm-forecasting techniques for hurricanes and tornadoes, through which people can be protected from the storms.

Carroll, Ruth and Latrobe   *Runaway Pony, Runaway Dog*

Beanie Tatum's pony, Sassy, and dog, Tough Enough, are staying at a faraway farm. They become homesick and experience many adventures as they make their way back home to Beanie.

Pattent, Dorothy Hinshaw   *A Picture Book of Ponies*

Ponies are popular in America. They have special qualities, are fun to ride, and also make good pets.

Reesink, Maryke   *The Fisherman's Family*

Jan's father is a fisherman whose boat doesn't return after a storm at sea. Jan helps his mother by selling toys he carves from driftwood until his father's boat returns.

WONDERING

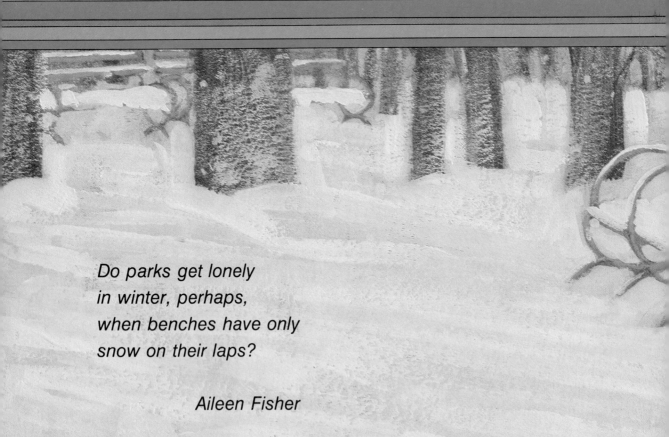

Do parks get lonely
in winter, perhaps,
when benches have only
snow on their laps?

Aileen Fisher

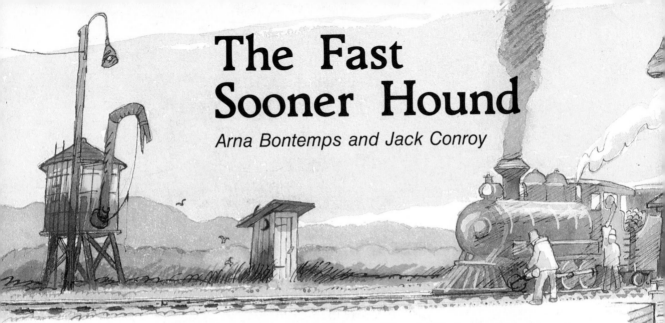

The Fast Sooner Hound

Arna Bontemps and Jack Conroy

A railroad man was walking down the street with his hands in his overall pockets, and a long-legged, lop-eared hound trotted behind him. After a while he stopped walking, and turned to the hound.

"Well, Sooner," he said, "here's the place."

They had come to a small building near the railroad tracks. Over the front door was a sign which said *Roadmaster*. The man opened the door and the hound followed him inside.

The man in the office looked up from his desk. 'What do you want?" he asked.

"I'm a Boomer fireman," the railroad man said, 'and I'm looking for a job."

"So you're a Boomer! Well, I know what that means. You go from one railroad to another."

"That's right," the man in overalls answered proudly.

"We might be able to use you on one of our trains," said the Roadmaster. "Have you got some place you can leave the dog?"

"Leave my dog!" cried the Boomer. "Listen here, Mr. Roadmaster, that Sooner always goes along with me."

"He does, eh? And why do you call him a Sooner?"

"He'd sooner run than eat—that's why. I raised him from a pup, and he's never spent a night or a day or even an hour away from me."

"I don't see how I can give you a job with the hound," the Roadmaster said. "It's against Rule Number One of the railroad to allow a passenger in the cab. Makes no difference if it's man or beast. It's a rule that's never been broken yet."

"Why, that's no trouble," said the Boomer. "The Sooner don't have to ride in the cab. He just runs alongside the train."

"You mean that old hungry-looking hound can outrun a freight train?" The Roadmaster laughed.

"Shucks—he'll do it without half trying," said the Boomer proudly.

"Oh, come now," said the Roadmaster. "The dog isn't born that can outrun one of our freight trains. We run the fastest freights from coast to coast. That's why we get so much business."

"Listen," said the Boomer, "my Sooner will run circles around your freight train. What's more, he'll be as fresh as a daisy when we pull into the junction."

"Well," said the Roadmaster, "you can have the job. I'm not a mean man, you know, but Rule One has got to stick."

So the Boomer fireman climbed into a cab beside the engineer and began to shovel coal for all he was worth. The freight train pulled out of the station and started to pick up speed. The Sooner loped along beside it. In no time at all he had left the freight train far behind.

The freight train made its run and then returned, but the Sooner led it all the way. And when the dog trotted into the Roadmaster's office a mile ahead of the train, the Roadmaster got angry. He was worried about what people would say about a freight train that couldn't keep up with a long-legged, lop-eared Sooner hound.

"Look here, Boomer," he said, as the fireman climbed down from the cab. "That Sooner outran the freight train, but I'm going to transfer you to a local passenger run. What do you think about that?"

"Suits me," said the Boomer. "Me and my Sooner take the jobs we get, and we always stay together."

"You think the hound can keep up with our passenger train?"

"He'll do it easy," said the Boomer. "No trouble at all."

So the race was on again. The Sooner speeded up to a trot as they pulled out of the station, and it seemed for a while that the passenger train might get ahead of him. But just as the race was getting exciting, the local train had to stop to pick up passengers. The Sooner came into the station ten minutes ahead of the local passenger train.

By that time people who lived along the railroad tracks were getting interested in the races. They came out of their houses to see the old Sooner hound. They began to think that something was surely wrong with the trains, but the trains were really right on schedule. They were keeping up their best speed. The trouble was with that old Sooner. He ran so fast he made the trains seem slow.

When the Roadmaster heard what the people thought about his trains, he got mad enough to bite the heads off nails. It would have to stop. Why, the people wouldn't ride the trains, and they were sending all their freight by trucks.

"Hey, Boomer," he said one day. "That Sooner of yours makes our trains look like snails."

"It isn't my Sooner that causes the trouble," said the Boomer. "It's that Rule Number One. My dog don't aim to give the road a black eye by outrunning the trains. He just aims to stay near me, that's all. Do away with the rule and let him ride with me in the cab, and everything will be O.K."

"Not on your life. That's the oldest rule on this road, and I don't plan to change it on account of an old lop-eared Sooner hound."

The Boomer shrugged his shoulders as he turned to walk away. "It's your railroad, Mr. Roadmaster," he said.

Before the Boomer and the hound were out of sight, the Roadmaster had a fine idea. "I'll fix that Sooner," he said, snapping his fingers. "I'll put the Boomer in the cab of our Cannon Ball. That's the fastest thing on wheels."

"You're going to a lot of trouble," the Boomer said to the Roadmaster, when he heard the plan. "There's no use for all this fuss. Just let my dog ride in the cab with me."

But the Roadmaster wouldn't change his plan. "I aim to see this race from the cab myself," he said, "but if that Sooner beats the Cannon Ball, I'll walk back, and he can have my seat."

Word got around that the Sooner was going to try to keep up with the Cannon Ball. People came from all over just like it was circus day, or the county fair.

Just before the starting whistle blew, the Roadmaster climbed into the cab of the Cannon Ball with the Boomer and the Engineer. He wanted to be sure that the Boomer shoveled plenty of coal and that the Engineer kept the fast train moving at top speed.

A clear track for a hundred miles was ordered for the Cannon Ball. The train pulled out of the station like a streak of lightning.

Every valve was popping off. The wheels rose three feet in the air above the roadbed. The Boomer shoveled coal for all he was worth, but he worked with a smile on his face. He knew his hound, and he didn't mind giving the dog a good run.

The Roadmaster stuck his head out of the cab window. Whoosh! Off went his hat—and he nearly lost his head too. He peered through the smoke and steam. Where was the Sooner? The Roadmaster couldn't see hide nor hair of him anywhere. He let out a whoop of joy.

"The SOONER! The SOONER!" he yelled. "He's *nowhere* in sight! This is the time we outran that old lop-eared hound."

"I can't understand that," the Boomer said. "That Sooner has never failed me before. Let me take a look."

He dropped his shovel and poked his head out of the window. He looked far and wide. The Roadmaster was right. The Sooner was nowhere to be seen. Where could he be?

The Roadmaster kept poking fun at the Boomer and laughing all the rest of the way to the station. But the Boomer didn't answer. Every moment or two he'd glance out of the window. Surely something was wrong. What had become of his Sooner?

Presently the station came into sight, and the Cannon Ball began to slow down.

A moment later the Boomer saw a great crowd of people around the station. He supposed they were waiting to cheer the Cannon Ball for making such a fast run. But no, they weren't even looking down the tracks. They were all watching something else.

The Engineer blew the whistle just before he brought the Cannon Ball to a stop. Still nobody paid any attention. The people were all looking the other way and laughing. The Boomer and the Roadmaster and the Engineer were all puzzled. They climbed down out of the cab.

"Well, here we are!" the Roadmaster cried, trying to get some attention. He pushed his way through the crowd. "What's going on here?" he insisted. "Didn't you people come down here to see the Cannon Ball?"

"Take it away," somebody answered. "It's too slow to catch cold. The Sooner's been here ten minutes and more."

The Boomer's heart gave a big jump when he heard that news. It seemed too good to be true. But a minute later he saw with his own eyes. Around the corner of the station came the old lop-eared hound, chasing a rabbit that he had rounded up along the way. He was having so much fun playing with the little creature and making the people laugh, that he had plumb forgot about the Cannon Ball.

"He's here!" the Boomer shouted. "He's here! My Sooner's true blue, and he's won again!"

The Roadmaster sputtered. "P-p-put him in the cab and get going."

"But where will *you* sit?" the Boomer asked with a grin.

"I'll walk," the Roadmaster answered. "Anything to stop that hound from outrunning our trains."

A few moments later the Boomer was back in the cab, his hound beside him, and the big crowd of people let out a great cheer as the Cannon Ball pulled out of the station for the home trip.

Just before the station went out of sight, the three in the cab of the Cannon Ball saw a man leave the crowd and begin to walk down the tracks. It was the Roadmaster starting for home.

Answer these questions.

1. Why was the fireman called a Boomer fireman?

2. Why did the Boomer fireman call his dog a Sooner?

3. Why did the railroad have Rule Number One?

4. What did the Roadmaster say he would do if the Sooner beat the Cannon Ball?

Maria's Cave

William H. Hooks

Maria's father, an archaeologist, attended an exposition in Paris in 1878. He saw tools, weapons, and jewelry made by people during the Stone Age. He became very excited because he believed there might be similar objects in the cave at Altamira near the family's summer home. The next summer he and his daughter, Maria, often explored the cave. If they found anything, they planned to show it to Professor Villanova, an expert on Stone Age objects.

In the weeks that followed, Maria went with Papa many times to the cave. There were good days when something turned up, but many days the floor of the cave yielded nothing at all.

Once Papa asked, "Wouldn't you rather stay home, Maria? Aren't you getting bored?"

"No, Papa. I love working in the cave with you. Every time we come to the cave, I think, *Today we are going to find something special.* It's just a feeling I have." She wavered. "That must sound silly."

"Silly? That's the same way I feel." They laughed and Papa said no more about going to the cave alone.

The collection of Stone Age things slowly grew. Besides the long needle and the necklace there were several stone ax heads, a few spear points, some flint scrapers, a bone knife, and a horn javelin.

Several times Papa said, "Soon I must take our finds from the cave to Professor Villanova." But he kept putting off the trip back to Madrid. Finally he told Mama, "I want to make one more trip to the cave; then we'll leave."

The next morning Maria felt a sadness come over her. This could be the last time she and Papa would ever visit the cave. They still hadn't found the "special thing" she always felt was going to turn up. And when they returned to Madrid, Papa would be gone all day, taking care of family business.

Inside the cave, Maria was restless. She wandered slowly around the large entrance chamber, looking at each section of the familiar room, as if saying good-bye. She passed the dark passageway at the back of the room, and soon she was near the pile of rocks which partly concealed the dark side room with the low ceiling. It was the room which she and Papa had so briefly explored. The wind made a low whistling sound as she walked by. Maria shivered, remembering how strange she felt in that mysterious room. For the first time she felt a strong urge to visit it again. She quickly walked over to where the box of candles was lying, picked one up, and lighted it.

The candle sputtered as Maria reapproached the rock-strewn entrance. She cupped it with her hand and pushed on into the pitch-black chamber. The candlelight sent wild, jagged shadows fleeing around the walls. The same chill and dampness which Maria remembered from the first visit surrounded her. Slowly she examined the floor for holes. Then she circled the walls with her candle, examined more of the floor, and soon had the plan of the room figured out. It was about twice as long as it was wide. Although the ceiling was low, she could stand upright in all but the far end, where the ceiling sloped down close to the floor.

She felt more at ease. At least the room didn't have underground streams or deep holes. She sat for a moment on a rock and began moving the candle around the walls, watching it make shapes like fantastic creatures as it bounced from one surface to another. She began to enjoy the game. She played with a tiger shape, making it leap from rock to rock. Suddenly she swept the candle across the ceiling. Her arm froze in midair.

A great eye was staring directly at her! This was no make-believe tiger. It was a real eye, looking straight at her from the ceiling. The candle trembled in her hand. Her mouth moved, but no sound came from her throat. She tilted the candle a little to one side. The staring eye was set in a great shaggy head. Somehow she managed to move her arm enough to see the whole shape. It looked like a huge bull charging from above. Maria circled the candle further along the ceiling. Another bull! And another! She found her voice.

"Bulls! Bulls! Bulls!" she cried.

Papa heard. "Maria! Where are you?" he shouted. He ran toward the entrance, thinking Maria had seen a stray bull outside the cave.

"Bulls! Bulls!" Maria shouted again. Papa turned back. The sound was coming from inside the cave. He stumbled across to the rocks and crawled through the dark entrance to the room where Maria was shouting.

"Papa, Papa! Look! Bulls!"

She was pointing toward the ceiling. He dropped to his knees to comfort her. From his knees he could look up at the ceiling.

"Bulls!" Maria whispered. She raised the candle and it was Papa's turn to become speechless. The great eye stared down at him. It seemed to blink as the candle flickered.

Papa reached for the candle and began moving it around the ceiling. More and more animals appeared. The ceiling was covered with a great herd of them.

Finally Papa spoke. "Maria, this cannot be." His voice quickened. "For thousands of years this cave has been sealed. Who could have done these paintings? Come, let's get more candles. We must take a better look."

Papa was already scrambling toward the passageway. Maria followed. They lit several candles and quickly returned. With the additional candlelight they could see larger portions of the ceiling. The painted animals looked alive. Some were running and galloping, others were standing still or asleep. The one with the great eye which had first stared out of the ceiling at Maria looked like a huge wounded bull. His head was pulled down and his hind legs were buckling underneath him.

"They look like they were just painted," said Maria. "The colors are so fresh. They look like they're still wet."

Papa reached up and touched one of the animals. He pulled his hand back into the candlelight. His fingers looked bloody! They were smeared with red paint.

"They *are* wet, Maria. The paint comes off when you touch it!" Then Papa said again, "This cannot be."

He studied the ceiling for a long time. He was so intent that Maria did not try to talk. Instead, she tried counting the animals in the big scene. It was hard because some of them were painted over parts of others. She counted more than twenty. They were mostly bulls, but there were some deer, a couple of horses, a wolf, and three animals that looked like pigs. As she studied the animals, Maria realized that the bulls looked different from any she had ever seen before.

"Papa, these are strange-looking bulls. What kind are they?"

"I've been thinking the same thing, Maria. They're not bulls at all. They're bison. And no bison have been seen in this part of the world for thousands of years." Then he muttered again, "This cannot be."

This time Maria responded to Papa's strange remark. "But, Papa, it *is*. The paintings are real. What do you mean, this cannot be?"

"Maria, I will say this only for your ears—anyone else would think I'm crazy. I believe you have discovered the first Stone Age paintings any living person has ever seen. If they were really painted thousands of years ago, this discovery will change our thinking about Stone Age people. This is not the work of unskilled artists."

Papa sounded so solemn. And yet Maria could feel the excitement in his voice.

"Come, Maria. We're going home. I must send a wireless message to Professor Villanova. It won't be necessary to take my finds from the cave to Madrid. The professor will come to us now. How could he resist?"

On the way home, Maria and Papa were silent. They were still overwhelmed by the discovery of the paintings. Papa finally spoke.

"Do you know what date today is, Maria?"

"Yes, Papa. It is the eighteenth of November, 1879."

"Remember that date, Maria. It could be the most important date in your life."

Later, Professor Villanova visited the cave and discovered why the paintings felt wet. The dampness of the cave had never allowed the paint to dry. The paintings were covered with a clear substance often found in caves that protected the paintings. He also found objects used by the artists. But he could not convince other scientists that the paintings were real Stone Age art. Years passed, but Maria never lost faith in the paintings. In 1902, some archaeologists finally came to see the cave paintings at Altamira and accepted them as genuine.

Answer these questions.

1. What feeling did Maria have every time she and her father went to the cave?

2. What game did Maria enjoy in the dark side room?

3. What important thing did Maria discover?

4. Why did Papa think Professor Villanova would choose to come to the cave?

5. Why did Papa think the date November 18, 1879, would be the most important date in Maria's life?

Words to Know in Science

Sometimes we see words in our science books that we haven't seen in our readers. Here are some words we might see in our science books.

Experiment	Liquid
Gas	Expands
Contracts	Solid
Thermometer	Scientist

Read these sentences with correct "science" words in the blanks. As you read, you will learn some important science facts. Then write the words on your paper.

1. A _____ measures temperature.

2. A person who is expert in observing and testing ideas is a _____.

3. An _____ helps scientists test new ideas.

4. Something that has a shape is a _____.

5. Something that can be poured is a _____.

6. Something that does not have a shape is a _____.

7. When something is hot, it _____ and gets larger.

8. When something is cold, it _____ and gets smaller.

Hi-Me

Pat Clyne

For a long time Jaime had wanted to come to the United States, but now that he was here, he wasn't enjoying it much at all. The main problem was the language.

Jaime was born in Argentina, where the people spoke Spanish, and though Jaime had learned some English in school before he came to the United States, it just wasn't enough.

One day Coach Gray introduced Jaime to the boys on the school football team.

"Come on, Jaime," Coach Gray said, "let's break the ice."

"Fine, but where is the ice?" Jaime answered, and of course the other boys laughed, just as they had laughed when they heard his name. It was really pronounced almost the same as "Hi-Me." But whenever the boys met him, they would say, "Hi, you, Hi-Me."

Jaime knew they were only teasing, and though he tried not to let it bother him, it bothered him a lot.

Another thing that bothered him was football. It was a game Jaime knew nothing about because in Argentina they played soccer, not football.

Coach Gray wanted Jaime to join the practice games, but Jaime always forgot what he was doing and wound up playing soccer instead of football. He tried to learn the rules, but there were so many that Jaime became confused. He couldn't say some of the strange football words, and when he tried to say them, the boys usually laughed at him.

Jaime was so embarrassed that he stopped trying to play football, and he even stopped trying to learn the rules of the game. What did it matter, anyway?

So Jaime just sat and watched, wishing he was back in Argentina, where they played soccer and spoke a language he could understand!

Coach Gray kept asking Jaime to join the football practice, but Jaime said "No." He knew the other boys didn't want him because they only laughed at him. But he didn't say that to Coach Gray; Jaime was too proud to do that.

He was also too proud to tell his father what was wrong, but Mr. Valda, somehow, knew. He wanted his son to learn to enjoy the United States.

"I go talk to boys," his father said one evening, "and I ask them to teach you football."

"No!" Jaime shouted. "Once they heard you talk, they . . ."

Jaime didn't finish his sentence.

"Maybe it is because I do not talk English so good?" Mr. Valda asked.

"Oh, no," Jaime said quickly, but inside he knew that was the reason. His father's English was even worse than his own, and if his father went to the boys, they would only laugh. They would laugh at both of them.

"I understand," Jaime's father said softly, "that my English is poor, but soon I learn more, Jaime. Until then, I will go watch boys play football, and maybe if I watch them, I can learn rules, and then I teach you."

"Remember, I was a good soccer player once," he said as he looked at Jaime.

Jaime felt tears in his eyes, and suddenly he was ashamed of himself because he had been ashamed of his father. And he was ashamed because his father had known how he felt.

"I would like you to watch the football," Jaime told his father. "We will go next Saturday and watch it together."

The next Saturday, as Jaime and his father sat on the bench watching the other boys play football, Jimmy Ellis ran over to the bench to get a drink of water. "Hi, you, Hi-Me!" Jimmy called, and went back to the game.

Then halftime was called, and the players were resting on the field.

"Come, Jaime," his father said, "I have the soccer ball in the car. If you cannot play football, at least you can play soccer."

Jaime smiled because he was tired of sitting on the hard bench, and it would be fun to play a little soccer before the football game started again.

Taking the soccer ball out of the car, Jaime and his father walked down to the end of the football field, where they began playing, kicking the ball, rolling and passing it to each other. Within a few minutes, Jaime was out of breath. He had forgotten what a good soccer player his father was.

He looked at his father and smiled, forgetting all about the other boys, football, and "Hi-Me." He forgot about Argentina and how he had wished he could be back there.

"Come, Jaime!" his father shouted. "Why do you stop so soon?" Jaime smiled as he ran to his father because he was very happy and very proud.

Jaime was just about to ask his father for a rest from their soccer match when he noticed that the other boys had gathered nearby and were watching Jaime and Mr. Valda carefully.

Just then Coach Gray came walking over to see what was happening.

As soon as Jaime's father introduced himself, Coach Gray asked, "Aren't you the Carlo Valda who played on the world-champion team about ten years ago?"

Mr. Valda nodded and said, "I am he."

"I'm proud to meet you," Coach Gray continued. "I heard a lot about you when you played on the team from Argentina."

Jaime's father smiled and said, "Thank you."

"I've always liked soccer; in fact, I wanted to start a soccer team here, but I just don't know enough about how to play the game," Coach Gray said.

"It would be an honor to help you learn," said Mr. Valda to the coach, "and Jaime could help me."

Jimmy Ellis came up, examined the soccer ball, and said, "It looks like it would be too hard to remember not to touch the ball with your hands."

"It's simple," Jaime laughed.

"Simple!" Jimmy said. "Maybe for you, but not for me. Say, Hi-Me, do you think you could—"

Jimmy was interrupted by Coach Gray saying, "Hey, fellows, I want you to meet the man who's going to teach us to play soccer, Jaime's father."

The cheer that came from the boys made Jaime's heart happy.

"I do not speak English so good," Jaime's father told them, "so you must teach me as I teach soccer to you—yes?"

"Maybe you can teach us a little Spanish, too," Jimmy Ellis suggested with enthusiasm.

Mr. Valda nodded and said, "We trade Spanish and soccer for English and football."

"You want to learn football too?" Jimmy asked, sounding confused.

"My son wants to learn football very much," Mr. Valda told him.

Jimmy looked puzzled and said, "But Hi-Me stopped playing with us so we didn't think he was interested."

Jaime stood there silently, so surprised that he couldn't think of anything to say in response to Jimmy's statement.

"We'll teach you, Hi-Me," Jimmy said, still saying Jaime's name as if it was two words instead of one.

Mr. Valda put one hand on Jaime's shoulder, the other hand on Jimmy's shoulder, and said, "Then it's a deal square."

"You mean a square deal," Coach Gray corrected. They all laughed, and Mr. Valda was laughing about his confused English right along with them. He didn't seem to be embarrassed, and suddenly smiling to himself, Jaime wasn't embarrassed either.

"By the way," Jimmy Ellis asked, "what's my name in Spanish?"

Jaime thought for a moment and he responded, "Jimmy is for James, and in Spanish, James is Jaime." Then he began laughing, as he said to Jimmy, "Hi, you, Hi-Me!"

Jimmy looked surprised, and then he laughed too, saying with enthusiasm, "Well, I hope this Hi-Me turns out to be as good a soccer player as you, Hi-Me."

He turned to Coach Gray and the other boys and shouted, "Come on, let's get to work!"

Answer these questions.

1. Why wasn't Jaime enjoying the United States?

2. Why did Jaime stop playing football and trying to learn the rules of the game?

3. How did Mr. Valda know what was troubling Jaime?

4. What did Mr. Valda and Jaime trade?

Write on your own.

Jaime and Jimmy became good friends because they were interested in each other. Pretend a family from another country has just moved next door to you. They don't speak much English. In five sentences tell how you would be friendly to a new child.

Janey by Moonlight

Eleanor Cameron

Janey woke with a start and stared down at the oblong of brilliant moonlight on the carpet. What had wakened her? Yes, the cats. Janey could hear the growling and hissing, broken by a snarling explosion of fury as they tangled with one another. Then silence: deep, utter silence. One of them must be lying dead while the other walked off, twitching its tail. But, no. There they went again, singing low and hating to begin with, then yowling higher and higher.

Janey bounced out of bed and trotted along the hall to her mother and father's bedroom. Daddy could go outside and stop them. There was a light under the door but no voices, because Mama was away visiting Aunt Lydia. Gently, Janey knocked, then called—no answer. She pushed open the door, and there was Daddy, book slipped down onto his stomach, eyes closed, head dropped over to one side while he snored slowly and peacefully. He was a deep, solid sleeper and Janey knew he was hard to waken.

Janey closed the door and went into the living room. She listened. Yes, the cats were still at it. She opened the front door, went out onto the veranda, yelled "SCAT!" and away shot two black shadows.

She stood there a moment, sniffing in the sharp fragrance of dry eucalyptus and pine needles, for Janey and her mother and father lived up in the Berkeley hills where the pine and oak and eucalyptus woods begin. Then she looked up and saw the moon, rather low in the sky, shining across Berkeley and the bay. Never had she seen such a moon! Why did it sometimes seem so much bigger and brighter when it was full than at other times? A mystery. She had just decided to go inside and get Daddy's binoculars from his desk drawer, when—

CLICK.

Her heart jumped. She didn't have to turn and look because she knew exactly what had happened. The minute she'd left the door open as she stepped out onto the porch, it had begun swinging closed, very, very slowly until, when it had finished its swing, the tongue of the lock slipped into place.

Every summer it was the same way. That old door stuck stubbornly all through the winter when it was rainy and the wood swelled. Then during late summer and fall, when the weather turned dry, the wood shrank and the door swung as if its hinges were oiled.

Janey knew it would be no use, but she went over and tried it. Not a hope. She rang the bell, good and long, but she knew quite well Daddy wouldn't hear, since the little bell was up over the kitchen door on the opposite side of the house. Mama would have—she always heard everything—but not Daddy.

She stood thinking about what she could do. Then she ran down the steps, along the driveway to the back, around into the garden, and over to Mama and Daddy's bedroom. The windows here at the back would be closed *and* locked, she knew, to be on the safe side, Daddy said. As for the two around the corner, which he always opened a little at night, there were so many big, thick, scratchy bushes under them, no one could possibly push a way in.

Quietly, quietly, like a little animal, she scratched at the window screen, which she could just reach. "*Daddy!*" she hissed, not very loud. "*Daddy*—it's me, Janey, and I'm locked out."

Why so quiet? Because of old Mrs. Leonard right on the other side of the fence, back up there in her apartment over the garage of the house next door. She'd been very sick and needed a lot of rest, so Janey had to be quiet.

But no matter how she scratched and called, as loud as she dared, Daddy went right on snoring.

She could go to the nice, kind couple in the house on the other side and ask them to phone Daddy. But the phone was in the dining room— he'd never hear. Could they call the landlady to come with a key? Oh, no, no! She lived clear over on the other side of Berkeley. And besides, she couldn't wake the Pearsons. It would be too mean— too embarrassing—and she wouldn't have the nerve.

Back she went to Daddy's window, got a stick, and forced it through the fragile, weathered screen. Then she began pushing it hard, back and forth, so that it made a thumping on the window.

Immediately, Daddy's snoring stopped. She thumped hard, twice. Silence, while he listened, trying to think. She could just see him, blinking, trying to get his wits together. "Daddy!" she called, "Let me in—"

Silence again, then, "Who—what is it? *What's going on?*" She bet he was still half-asleep.

"It's me, Daddy—Janey. I'm out here."

Another silence, while he must have been trying to make sense of this. "Janey? Out where?"

"Outside—"

"*Outside! Where outside?*"

"In the garden—"

"In the *garden!*" And he came over and unlocked the window and pulled it up. "What in the dickens," he demanded indignantly, "are you doing out in the garden at this time of night? Why, it must be two in the morning—"

"I know. But some cats woke me up, and I went to chase them away and look at the moon, and the door closed on me, and I'm locked out."

Daddy groaned. "You crazy kid, telling me you're looking at the moon at two in the morning. I've told you time and again to watch that door if you don't have your key. And I was fast asleep—"

He put down the window, latched it, and went off. Naturally she expected him to come to the back door, but she waited and he didn't. Oh, of course—he'd just gone right on through the living room to the front as *his* quickest way to let her in. So she scudded around the side, along the drive, and up onto the porch, and there he was, standing at the door.

"Janey, Janey!" he said. "What if you hadn't been able to wake me up? Your mother says there could be an explosion and I'd sleep right through it."

Janey went to him and threw her arms around him, then took his hand and pulled him onto the veranda. "Look!" she said. "Just look! Did you ever see such a beautiful moon in your life?"

And Daddy stood there with her at the railing, looking out at that incomparable moon. And behind them, the door went—CLICK.

Answer these questions.

1. Why did Janey knock on her father's door?

2. What happened just as Janey decided to go back inside?

3. Why did Janey have to be quiet?

4. Why was her father surprised to see Janey outside his window?

About the Author

Eleanor Cameron writes children's books, among them the Mushroom Planet series. She has won several awards, including the National Book Award for *The Court of the Stone Children.*

City

In the morning the city
Spreads its wings
Making a song
In stone that sings.

In the evening the city
Goes to bed
Hanging lights
About its head.

Langston Hughes

About the Author

Langston Hughes was born in Missouri and raised in Kansas and Illinois. He began to write poetry in high school after his classmates elected him the class poet. His poems have been translated into six languages, and many have been set to music.

Words to Know in Recipes

If you like to cook, you will sometimes need to read a recipe. In some recipes you will see abbreviations used for words that show measurements. Here are some abbreviations you should know.

teaspoon = t. or tsp.

tablespoon = T., tbs., or tbsp.

cup = c.

package = pkg.

ounces = oz.

pound = lb.

Rewrite these ingredients for tacos. Write out the complete measurement words in place of the abbreviations.

TACOS SEALED WITH REFRIED BEANS

1 lettuce wedge, chopped
1 c. chopped tomatoes
1 pkg. (10 oz.) cheddar cheese, shredded
1 lb. ground beef
3 T. minced onion
1 can (8 oz.) tomato sauce
1 t. garlic salt
1 t. chili powder
dash of pepper
1 can (15 oz.) refried beans
1 pkg. (5 oz.) taco shells

Vocabulary Review

Read each sentence and the four answers that follow it. Decide which answer best completes the sentence. Write the answer on your paper.

1. A schedule tells the _____ that things are to be done.
   a. time
   b. reason
   c. temperature
   d. way

2. To be solemn is to be _____.
   a. serious
   b. solid
   c. frightened
   d. loud

3. When something is confused, it is _____.
   a. mixed-up
   b. concealed
   c. important
   d. beautiful

4. When there is enthusiasm about something, there is _____.
   a. embarrassment
   b. boredom
   c. calmness
   d. excitement

5. A veranda is a _____ that goes around a house.
   a. verse
   b. porch
   c. roof
   d. staircase

Books to Read

Berenstain, Stan and Jan   *The Berenstain Bears' Science Fair*

Small Bear and Sister Bear want to make something to take to a science fair. Papa Bear helps them learn about machines, matter, and energy.

Foster, Sally   *A Pup Grows Up*

This book pictures many different puppies and then shows how they will look when they are grown. It also lists many facts about dogs.

Gackenbach, Dick *The Dog and the Deep Dark Woods*

The animals in the woods find a boot, a kettle, and a plate. When a dog tries to tell the animals what the articles are, they laugh at the dog. The dog then goes to live with people, and has been doing so ever since.

Moore, Eva *The Great Banana Cookbook for Boys and Girls*

This is a cookbook that gives eleven delicious recipes that use bananas.

REMEMBERING

Into my heart's treasury
    I slipped a coin
That time cannot take
    Nor thief purloin,—
Oh, better than the minting
    Of a gold-crowned king
Is the safe-kept memory
    Of a lovely thing.

Sara Teasdale

222

Thomas A. Edison

Curtis P. Washington

When he was young, some people considered Thomas Alva Edison an unusual boy. Maybe the reason was that he was always asking questions. He had great curiosity about his surroundings. If no one would answer his questions, he could find his own answers!

One day Al—as his family occasionally called him—noticed that a hen could hatch chicks by sitting on eggs. A few days later, Al was found sitting on a nest of eggs, attempting to hatch some baby chicks. Of course, his experiment failed!

But that didn't mean that Al was going to stop learning, or asking questions. His mother showed him that learning could be fun by making a game of teaching him to read. Al had never enjoyed anything so much, and soon he was reading one book after another.

Al started school at the age of seven but attended only three months. From that time his mother became his teacher.

When Al was nine years old, his mother gave him a chemistry book. He set up his own laboratory and began doing all the experiments that were in the textbook. He had to find out for himself whether the man who wrote the chemistry book was correct.

When Al was twelve years old, he got a job as a "news butcher" on a train, selling newspapers, sandwiches, and peanuts. He needed the job so he could earn money to buy chemicals and other supplies for his experiments.

In one car of the train Al set up a little shop so that in his spare time he could work on his experiments. He even printed his own newspaper —the first to be published on a moving train.

But one day something awful happened to Al! Some of the jars of chemicals in his shop on the train overturned, bursting into flames and setting the train car on fire.

The train conductor was furious, and he severely scolded Al.

Later on, Edison began to lose his hearing. He blamed his deafness on another accident that occurred on a train.

In time his deafness worsened. A doctor wanted to operate on Edison's ears, but Edison wouldn't allow an operation.

"I don't mind being deaf," he said. "It's easier to think about my experiments and inventions if I can't hear all the noise around me."

After Thomas Edison lost his first train job, he traveled around the country, working at odd jobs when and where he could. During this time he invented a voting machine that could record everyone's vote. But when Edison tried to sell his machine, no one was interested. Edison made a promise to himself. "I'll never again invent something that no one wants," he said. Edison kept that promise he had made to himself. However, some states today use a voting machine similar to the one Edison invented and no one wanted.

When Edison was twenty-two years old, he arrived in New York City with little money and no place to sleep. A very kind gentleman let Edison sleep in his office, and in return, Edison helped the man when he could.

One day a machine broke down. After other people attempted to fix the machine and weren't successful, Edison made it operate again. The man was so happy with what Edison had done that he employed him at $300 a month.

Edison liked to repair old machines. He also worked on his own inventions and made new machines. The boss at one company, Mr. Lefferts, was fascinated by Edison's new machines. One day he asked Edison, "How much money would you take for your machines?"

"Well," thought Edison to himself, "I could ask for $5,000 and hope to get $3,000. What shall I say?" At last he said, "Well, Mr. Lefferts, how much would you like to pay for my machines?" Now it was Mr. Lefferts's turn to think. "How would $40,000 be, Mr. Edison?" he asked.

Edison could hardly believe what he was hearing. At last he would have all the money he needed to work on his experiments and inventions! "Yes," he answered slowly, "I think that will be fine."

Only twenty-three years old at this time, he used the money from Mr. Lefferts to set up a large laboratory. He hired many people to work for him, and he worked more than any of them. He improved the typewriter, and in 1876 he improved Alexander Graham Bell's invention, the telephone.

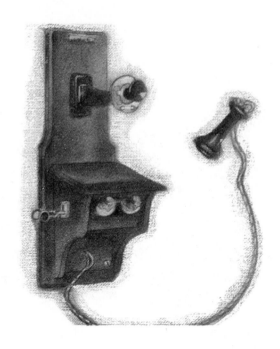

Before Edison worked on the telephone, people had to shout into it to be heard on the other end of the line. Edison made a telephone that would carry voices a long way even when people spoke normally.

The beginning of one of Edison's greatest inventions, the phonograph, started with a drawing of a machine. Edison gave the drawing to John, one of the men working for him, to build. John was puzzled. He couldn't understand what the machine was meant to be, but in a day or two he had it ready and he took it to Edison.

"This machine is going to talk," said Edison as he wrapped a piece of tin foil around one part of it. He called everyone over to listen.

Edison got close to the machine and said, "Mary had a little lamb." When he stopped talking, the machine played back what Edison had said. The people couldn't believe their ears!

Edison worked on many other projects. He made a light bulb and the first moving-picture machine that was successful. He received many awards for his inventions.

He kept on working to the end of his life. When he died in 1931 at the age of 84, he had invented over 1,100 things.

Answer these questions.

1. Why did people think Thomas Edison was an unusual boy?

2. What did Edison's mother show him about learning?

3. Why was Edison surprised when Mr. Lefferts offered him $40,000 for his machines?

4. Why did Edison receive many awards?

A Song of Greatness

(A Chippewa Indian Song)

When I hear the old men
Telling of heroes,
Telling of great deeds
Of ancient days,
When I hear them telling,
Then I think within me
I too am one of these.
When I hear the people
Praising great ones,
Then I know that I too
Shall be esteemed,
I too when my time comes
Shall do mightily.

Transcribed by Mary Austin

Electricity— Sound and Light

Anne Cappy

Flip a switch and a light goes on. It's simple, right? Wrong! Every time you flip a light switch, you make billions of little electrons go to work for you. Uncountable hours of work have gone into providing you with the electricity you need to turn that light on. Without electricity you wouldn't have telephones, television, video games, and many other things you use every day.

What is Electricity?

Have you ever gotten a shock when you touched a doorknob, or seen sparks fly when you combed your hair? That's electricity.

Electricity is a type of energy that gives things the power to work. This energy comes from electrons. Scientists have learned how to use electrons to produce electricity.

How Does It Work?

It takes billions of electrons to make electricity operate. Electrons move through an electric wire in much the same way water moves through a garden hose. Turning on the faucet pushes the water through the hose. Pushing electrons makes electricity move through the wire.

The machine that pushes the electrons through the wire is called a generator. The wire from the generator goes to your home and into a control center, which is either a fuse box or a circuit breaker.

The fuse box controls how much electricity you use. If you try to use too much, you will "blow a fuse," and the electricity from that fuse will be cut off. A circuit breaker works differently from a fuse box. A circuit breaker does not let you use too much electricity. It cuts off the flow before there's an overload. If you did not have a fuse box or circuit breaker, your electric wires could overheat and start a fire!

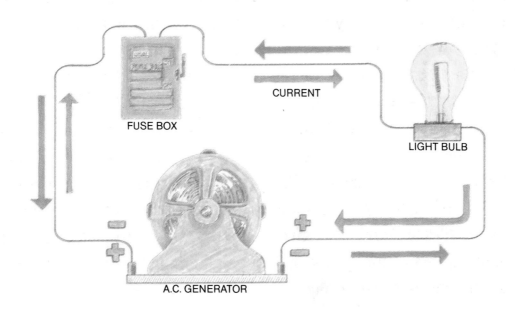

FUSE BOX

CURRENT

LIGHT BULB

A.C. GENERATOR

From the fuse box or circuit breaker, the wires go inside your walls to light switches and sockets. Turning on the light switch lets the electricity flow to the light, and the light goes on. When you put a plug into a socket, electricity comes to the socket. But it doesn't flow into the lamp until the switch is turned on.

How Can We Use It?

Besides turning on lights, we can use electricity to carry sound. Sound is made by vibrations called sound waves. The electricity in a telephone picks up the sound waves from the speaker on one end and carries them to the receiver on the other end. The electricity moves so fast that you can hardly notice the time it takes to travel from one place to another.

When you turn on your TV, you get both light and sound. Again, it is electricity that makes this possible, allowing you to see and hear your favorite shows!

What Does It Do?

Electricity makes so many things possible. Most of our food comes from farms that use machinery that runs on electricity. Most of our clothes are made in factories that need electricity to operate.

It is hard to imagine what our lives would be like without electricity. Scientists have worked for hundreds of years to bring electricity to us, and are still working to find new and better ways to produce the electricity that makes so many things happen.

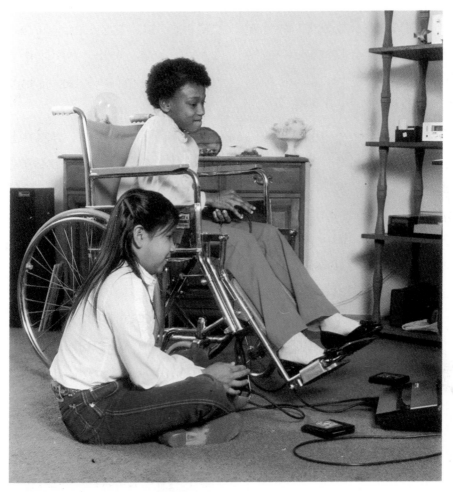

Answer these questions.

1. How have scientists learned to produce electricity?

2. What does a generator do?

3. What could happen if you did not have a fuse box or circuit breaker in your home?

4. What can electricity do besides turning on lights?

5. Why are scientists still working to find new and better ways to produce electricity?

Talking Leaves

Mary Yellowhair

How could the word of such a madman be trusted?

The Cherokee chiefs shook their heads and laughed at Sequoyah as he stood before them. They reminded each other that Sequoyah wasn't really one of them because he was only half Cherokee, his mother having been an Indian, and his father a white man. Even worse, Sequoyah had been a soldier in the white man's army when he was a young man.

The year was 1821 when Sequoyah stood before the most important Cherokee chiefs and announced that he could make "talking leaves." How could anyone make words come from leaves?

With Sequoyah was his daughter, Ah-Yoka, who was barely twelve years old. Sequoyah had tried to make them believe that even she could make talking leaves, but how could this frightened child, who hid behind her father, make such powerful medicine?

No, the chiefs didn't believe Sequoyah could be trusted. By trying to make jokes with them, he was making bad medicine, so the chiefs became angry, and they frowned and murmured to each other.

Sequoyah tried to explain why talking leaves were necessary to the Cherokees. He told how he had first learned of talking leaves when he was in the army and saw the white soldiers look at pieces of paper with strange markings. These markings told them news of events that had occurred far away.

Sequoyah reminded the chiefs that the Cherokee people were now scattered across the country. If they were ever again to be united, they must be able to communicate.

Sequoyah told the chiefs that he'd worked for twelve years and had turned the many sounds of the Cherokee language into only eighty written symbols. He believed that all Cherokee people could understand them, and that by writing the symbols on leaves of paper, they could communicate with others far away.

After discussing among themselves, the chiefs made their decision—they would prove once and for all that Sequoyah was a madman. They would put him to a test, and when he failed, he would be punished.

Sequoyah was frightened, because if he failed the test Ah-Yoka might be punished as well. It had seemed only right that she should be here with him, since she had been a great help in his work.

Sequoyah's wife had become angry because he had spent so much time writing on pieces of bark, so she had burned the bark and turned him out of his home. Ah-Yoka had remained with her father even when angry Indians who feared his strange medicine burned their new home. And it had been Ah-Yoka who had found a white man's spelling book in the woods. Because she understood her father's work completely, she knew that the spelling book would be valuable to Sequoyah.

240

And it had been valuable, because after studying the alphabet in the spelling book, Sequoyah made a set of symbols for the Cherokee language. Sequoyah's system wasn't an alphabet, however. Because the written symbols stood for different sounds, the system was called a syllabary. Since Sequoyah's young daughter had been able to learn all the symbols, he was certain that Cherokee Indians everywhere could learn them.

Although he was nervous about the chiefs' decision, Sequoyah remembered how hard he had worked for this moment. He had come across the country to inform the chiefs about the syllabary. He thought about how the scattered Cherokee people might never again be a united people because they couldn't communicate with each other. He decided he must go through with the test.

It wasn't a difficult test. Sequoyah was told to wait outside the council house while, inside, the chiefs told Ah-Yoka some words to write down on paper. Sequoyah waited and worried, until at last the door was opened and he was told to come inside. As Sequoyah took the piece of paper, he glanced at his daughter and was relieved to see that she no longer looked fearful.

Then he looked at the piece of paper and read aloud the words that were written on it. He could tell by the faces of the chiefs that he had made no mistake, that every word had been correct. The chiefs were delighted because they had spoken to a man who was too far away to hear their words. At last they knew what it was like to have a language that could be written as well as spoken. It took them only three days of studying to learn Sequoyah's syllabary.

Sequoyah was relieved to learn that he was to be rewarded instead of punished. He had not failed, and he was happy to have proved that he was not a madman.

Sequoyah was rewarded more, however, by seeing the Cherokee people communicate by using his syllabary. Within a few years it was being used across the country, and everyone realized that Sequoyah's medicine was good for the Cherokee people.

Answer these questions.

1. Why wasn't Sequoyah accepted as one of the Cherokees?

2. What did Sequoyah tell the Cherokee chiefs he could do?

3. What did the scattered Cherokee people need if they were to be united?

4. Why were the Cherokee chiefs delighted with the results of the test?

5. Why did the Cherokee chiefs call the pieces of paper with words on them "talking leaves"?

Write on your own.

While walking in the woods, Ah-Yoka, Sequoyah's daughter, found a white man's spelling book. Write five sentences telling Ah-Yoka's exciting experience of finding the book and showing it to her father.

Words to Know at the Grocery Store

Have you been shopping at a grocery store? You probably saw these words on signs there.

Dairy foods

Fresh produce

Meats, poultry, seafoods

Bakery

Pet foods

Household cleansers

On your paper draw six grocery signs using the six categories. Leave a lot of space below each sign. Write each of these items under the sign where you think it would be found in the grocery store.

Window cleaner	Milk
Cauliflower	Shrimp
Hamburger buns	Apples
Laundry detergent	Dog food
Cheddar cheese	Bleach
Ground beef	Cottage cheese
Green peppers	Lettuce
Bird seed	Chicken
Round steak	Yogurt
Strawberries	Buttermilk
Furniture polish	Raisin bread
Hot dog buns	Cat food
Watermelon	Liver
Whole wheat bread	Floor wax

Make a Poster

Jeanette Cook

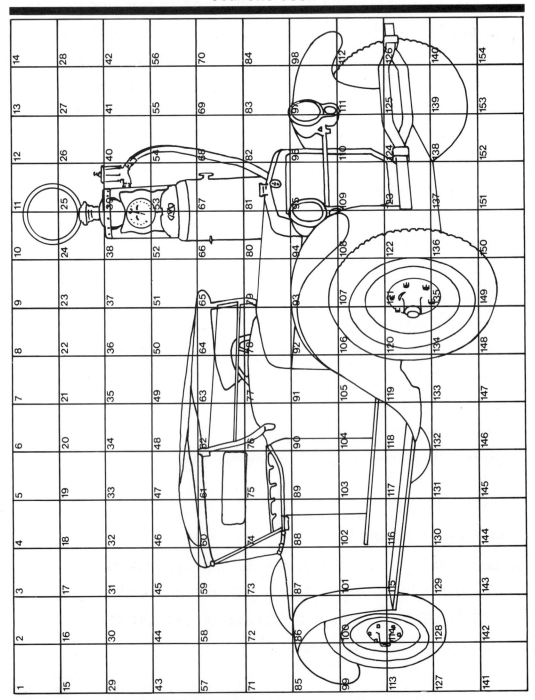

Turn your book and look at the automobile on page 246. It may look like just an old car to you, but to a collector of rare automobiles, it is very special. It is a 1922 Wills Sainte Claire roadster. Although about 16,000 Sainte Claires were made during the twenties, only about 75 still exist.

While some people enjoy restoring old automobiles like this one, other people like to collect posters of them. If you would like a poster of this Sainte Claire to hang in your room, you can make it yourself.

You will need these things:

a photocopy of the picture on page 246
a piece of white poster board, 22 inches by 28 inches
a pencil
a yardstick
a large, soft eraser
crayons, tempera paints, or felt-tip pens

Directions:
1. Look closely at the photocopy. You can see that the drawing of the roadster is on a grid 14 squares wide and 11 squares deep. The squares on the grid are numbered from 1 to 154.

2. On a large, flat surface, place the poster board with a long side at the top. Using the yardstick and pencil, mark off 2-inch spaces across each long side to divide the width of the poster into 14 spaces.

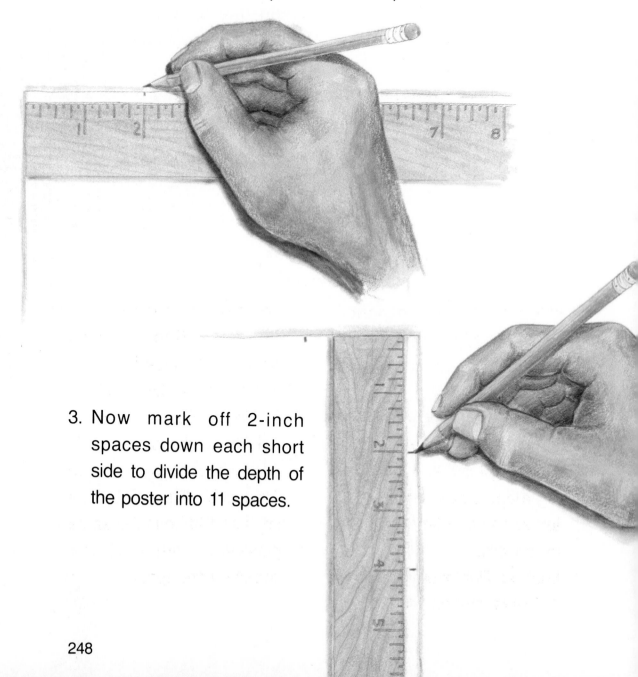

3. Now mark off 2-inch spaces down each short side to divide the depth of the poster into 11 spaces.

4. Using the yardstick and pencil, connect the poster board marks to make a grid with 154 squares. These squares will be much larger than those on the photocopy.

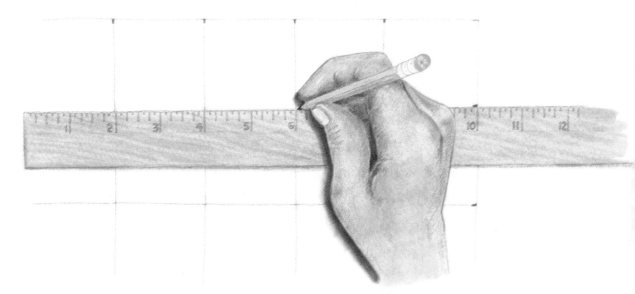

5. Moving from left to right, lightly number the poster board squares from 1 to 154.

6. Now forget about copying a large, complicated picture. Instead, think about copying many small, simple pictures, one at a time, square by square.

7. Look at Photocopy Square 1. There are no lines in it, so move from left to right until you find the first square with lines in it. It is in Photocopy Square 10.

8. In Poster Square 10, carefully draw the same kinds of lines that you see in Photocopy Square 10. The lines should be in the same positions, but they will occupy more space.

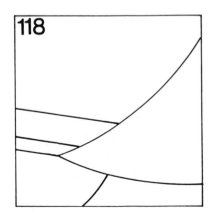

9. Compare the two squares carefully. If Poster Square 10 does not look like a larger version of Photocopy Square 10, erase it and try again.

10. Continue making one picture at a time, one square at a time. Check each finished poster square against the corresponding photocopy square.

11. When you have finished copying the whole automobile and the gas pump behind it, erase the grid lines and numbers.

12. After checking the overall drawing and straightening any "bumps" in your lines, add colors and background.

Now that you know how to use a small picture to make a large poster, you may want to try a picture of another subject—a horse, a spaceship, or a comic book character, for example. Use a photocopy of the picture you choose, because you will have to mark it off in a grid of equal squares.

You may discover that making posters is more fun than buying them!

Answer these questions.

1. What makes a Wills Sainte Claire roadster special?

2. Why do some people collect rare automobiles?

3. Why is a photocopy used to make a poster?

4. Why is it easier to draw the picture in many small pictures instead of one large picture?

The Golden Touch

Nathaniel Hawthorne

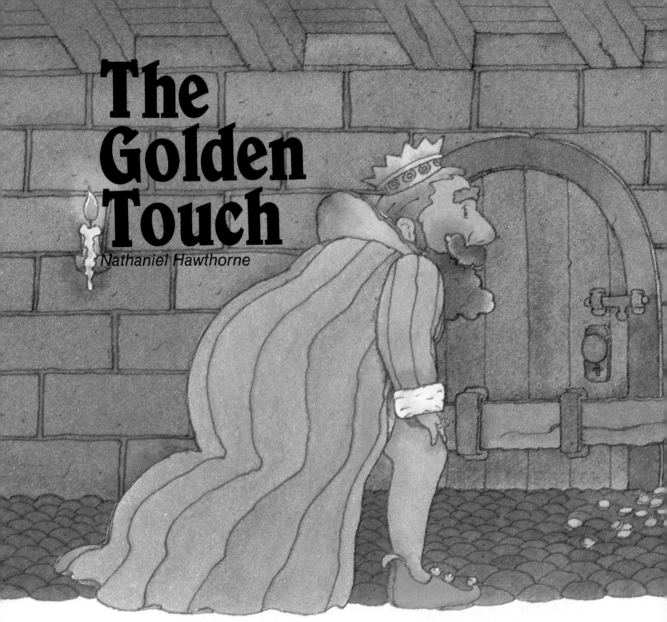

Once upon a time there lived a very wealthy king named Midas.

King Midas was fonder of gold than of anything else in the world. If he loved anything better, it was his daughter, Marygold. But the more he adored his daughter, the more he wanted to save her all the riches he could.

As days passed, Midas got to be so greedy that he could hardly stand to see or touch anything that was not gold. He spent almost every day in a dark room in the basement of his palace where he kept his riches. After carefully locking the door, he would gather gold coins and bring them into the one bright and narrow sunbeam that fell from the window. The only reason he loved that sunbeam was that his treasure would not shine without its aid.

Midas was in his treasure room one day when a shadow fell over the heaps of gold. King Midas quickly looked up, and saw a strange young man standing in the sunbeam.

"You are wealthy, King Midas," the stranger said. "No other room on earth contains as much gold and riches as you have in this room."

"I have done rather well," answered Midas, "but I could always use more."

"If you're not satisfied, what would satisfy you?" asked the stranger.

Midas thought about it for a moment. "I wish that everything I touch would change to gold!" King Midas exclaimed.

"The Golden Touch!" the stranger said. "That's a brilliant idea, but are you absolutely sure that this will satisfy you?"

"How could it fail?" said Midas.

"As you wish, then," replied the stranger. "Tomorrow, at sunrise, you will find yourself gifted with the Golden Touch."

The next morning, when the earliest sunbeam shone through the window onto his bedspread, King Midas looked closely and found that his bedspread had been changed into a fine gold cloth. The Golden Touch had come!

Midas leaped out of bed and ran about the room touching everything. He quickly put on his clothes and was delighted to see himself in a gorgeous suit of gold cloth.

He went downstairs, lifted the door latch (brass only a moment ago, but golden when he touched it), and went into the rose garden. How he loved the delicate roses!

But Midas knew a way to make the roses far more precious than they had ever been before. He went from bush to bush and touched each flower and changed them to gold. Rather pleased with his efforts, he went back inside.

Before long he heard Marygold sobbing, and he was upset, because Marygold was a happy girl.

"What is the matter with you this sunny morning?" asked Midas.

Marygold held out one of the roses that Midas had changed to gold.

"Beautiful!" exclaimed her father. "And why does this golden rose make you weep?"

"It is not beautiful but the ugliest flower that ever grew! As soon as I was dressed, I ran into the garden to gather some roses for you because I know you enjoy them. But all the beautiful roses, that smelled so sweetly and had so many lovely colors, are yellow and no longer have any smell! What is the matter with them?"

"My dear little girl, don't cry about it!" said Midas, who was ashamed to say that he himself had turned all the roses to gold. "Don't you see that a golden rose is much more valuable than one that would wither in a day?"

"I don't care for such roses," cried Marygold, tossing it away, "that have no smell, and hard petals that prick my nose!"

King Midas reached over to comfort his daughter and gave her a kiss.

"My dear, dear Marygold!" he cried.

But Marygold couldn't answer.

What had he done? The moment the lips of Midas touched Marygold's forehead, a change had occurred, and her sweet, rosy face and beautiful brown hair had turned yellow. Because of his desire for wealth, little Marygold was no longer a child, but a golden statue.

It was a favorite saying of Midas's that Marygold was worth her weight in gold. But now, when it was too late, he felt how much more valuable she was to him than all the riches on earth.

Midas couldn't do anything except wring his hands, and wish that he were the poorest man in the world if the loss of all his wealth might bring back his Marygold.

He suddenly saw a stranger standing in the door. Midas bent down his head quietly, for he knew it was the same figure who had appeared to him and given him the Golden Touch.

"Why are you so miserable?" inquired the man.

"I've found out that gold is not everything," answered Midas, "and I've lost all that my heart really cared for."

"Ah! So you've made a discovery since yesterday!" said the stranger. "Which of these two do you think is really worth the most—the gift of the Golden Touch or your Marygold?"

"Oh, my child!" cried poor Midas.

"You are wiser than you were, King Midas," said the stranger. "Go, then, and plunge into the river below your garden, and take a vase of the water and sprinkle it over whatever you want to change back again from gold."

King Midas bowed low, and when he lifted his head, the stranger had vanished.

Midas lost no time in snatching up a large vase and running to the riverside, where he plunged headfirst into the river.

He dipped the vase into the water and quickly ran back to the palace. The first thing he did was sprinkle the water by handfuls over the golden statue of little Marygold.

No sooner did it fall on her than the rosy color came back to her face, and she was surprised to find herself dripping wet and her father still tossing more water over her!

Next he led little Marygold into the garden, where he sprinkled water over the roses. They once again bloomed in gorgeous colors and smelled as sweet as ever.

From then on, King Midas hated all gold except for his Marygold's golden hair which remained that color to remind him of the Golden Touch.

Answer these questions.

1. Why did King Midas keep all his riches in a dark room in the basement?

2. What did King Midas want to do for his daughter?

3. What wish did King Midas make?

4. Why did Marygold cry?

5. Why was King Midas so miserable?

Memory

Memory is a tape recorder
And there's one in every head
Storing everything we've ever seen,
Or felt, or heard, or said.
The word, *remember,* simply means
We're playing back a part
Of all that's been recorded there
And lives close to our heart.
Sad thing, sweet thing,
Whatever it be,
The calling it back is a
Memory.

Mary O'Neill

Words to Know about Health

We are all interested in good health. We can read about good health in books and magazines. Here are some words we should know as we study about health.

Vitamins   Germs
Exercise   Lungs
Nutrition   Heart
Immunizations   Muscles

Number your paper from 1 to 8. Choose the best word to complete each sentence. Write the words on your paper.

1. _____ makes muscles strong.
   Relaxing   Skin   Exercise

2. _____ help make bones move.
   Feet   Muscles   Lungs

3. _____ are very small living things that can make us sick.
   Bones   Muscles   Germs

4. _____ are given to prevent some diseases.
   Colds   Immunizations   Germs

5. Good _____ is important to good health.
   skin   nutrition   soap

6. _____ are found in most fruits and vegetables.
   Muscles   Lungs   Vitamins

7. The _____ furnish the body with fresh air.
   lungs   ears   teeth

8. The _____ pumps blood through the body.
   air   heart   mouth

Vocabulary Review

Read each sentence and the four answers that follow it. Decide which answer best completes the sentence. Write the answer on your paper.

1. A person who is puzzled about something is _____.
   - a. confused
   - b. smart
   - c. hassled
   - d. excited
2. When you communicate with another person, you _____.
   - a. hum
   - b. talk
   - c. educate
   - d. concentrate
3. The width of something is how _____ it is.
   - a. tall
   - b. warm
   - c. wide
   - d. deep
4. Something that is complicated to figure out is _____.
   - a. complete
   - b. simple
   - c. difficult
   - d. delicate
5. That wealthy gentleman has a lot of _____.
   - a. food
   - b. time
   - c. riches
   - d. energy

Books to Read

Bleeker, Sonia *The Cherokee Indians of the Mountains*

The details of daily life, customs, legends, and ceremonies of the Cherokee Indians are presented through a ball game between two villages. The history of this famous tribe includes a chapter on Sequoyah.

Murphy, Jim *Weird & Wacky INVENTIONS*

Each invention presented is a quiz that is challenging and fun. Simple and clear explanations are provided on how the inventions worked or failed.

Pine, Tillie S., and Levine, Joseph *Electricity and How We Use It*

This book explains where electricity comes from, what it is, and how it works for us in our daily lives. Simple and easy-to-do experiments are included.

Wilkinson, Sylvia *Automobiles*

The invention of cars has led people to travel faster and farther than before. Today there are many kinds of cars. Caring properly for cars and obeying safety rules are important for car owners.

IMAGINING

What will you find at the edge of the world?
A footprint,
a feather,
desert sand swirled?
A tree of ice,
a rain of stars,
or a junkyard of cars?

Eve Merriam

271

The Wizard of Oz

L. Frank Baum
Adapted by Lynne Sharon Schwartz

Cast

NARRATOR

DOROTHY

WITCH OF THE NORTH

TWO MUNCHKINS

SCARECROW

TIN WOODMAN

COWARDLY LION

TOTO

CAPTAIN

OZ, THE WIZARD

WICKED WITCH OF THE WEST

KING OF THE WINGED MONKEYS

GLINDA, *the Good Witch of the South*

AUNT EM

274

Going to See the Wizard

NARRATOR: Once upon a time there was a little girl named Dorothy, who lived in Kansas with her uncle Henry, her aunt Em, and her dog, Toto. One day they heard the wailing wind, and they knew that a cyclone was coming. Uncle Henry ran out to take care of the cattle, and Aunt Em ran to a trapdoor in the floor, calling for Dorothy to follow her. At that moment, Toto jumped out of Dorothy's arms and hid under the bed. As Dorothy reached to get him, the house shook so hard that she fell down on the floor. Then the house started whirling around and slowly rose through the air, and was carried miles and miles up into the air. The wind was shrieking loudly, but soon the house felt very calm, and Dorothy crawled into her bed and fell asleep. When she woke up, she found herself in a strange place with Toto beside her.

SETTING: *A field with a house. Two silver shoes can be seen sticking out from under the house.*

DOROTHY: I wonder where I am! All I can remember is whirling around and around.

WITCH OF THE NORTH: You are most welcome to
the land of the Munchkins. Your house fell on
the Wicked Witch of the East, and now she is
dead. Those are her two feet sticking out from
under the house.

DOROTHY: Oh, dear! I'm in the land of the Munchkins? Who are the Munchkins?

WITCH OF THE NORTH: They are the people who
live in this land of the East. These are two of
my Munchkin friends. I am the Witch of the
North.

DOROTHY: Oh, gracious! Are you a real witch?

WITCH OF THE NORTH: Yes, but I'm a good witch.

DOROTHY: I thought all witches were wicked.

WITCH OF THE NORTH: Oh, no. There were four
　　witches in all the Land of Oz. Two of them,
　　those who live in the North and the South, are
　　good witches. Those who lived in the East and
　　the West were wicked witches. Now that the
　　Wicked Witch of the East is dead, there is just
　　one Wicked Witch left.

1ST MUNCHKIN: Look! The Wicked Witch of the
　　East's feet have disappeared. Only the silver
　　shoes are left.

WITCH OF THE NORTH: She was so old that she
　　dried up quickly in the sun. Now the silver
　　shoes are yours to wear.

2ND MUNCHKIN: These silver shoes have a charm,
　　but we have never known what it is.

DOROTHY *(Puts on the shoes):* Thank you. Now can you help me find my way back to Kansas?

WITCH OF THE NORTH *(Takes off her hat):* Perhaps we will get a message from my hat to help us. *(Reads the message)* The message says, "Let Dorothy go to the Emerald City." Is your name Dorothy?

DOROTHY: Yes. Where is the Emerald City?

WITCH OF THE NORTH: It is in the center of the country, and is ruled by Oz, the Great Wizard.

DOROTHY: How can I get there?

WITCH OF THE NORTH: You must walk. It is a long, terrible journey, but I will keep you from harm. When you get to Oz, tell him your story and ask him to help you. Goodbye.

DOROTHY: Goodbye, and thank you. (DOROTHY *walks around. The* SCARECROW *comes on stage. She walks by the* SCARECROW.)

SCARECROW: Good day.

DOROTHY: Did you speak?

SCARECROW: Certainly. How do you do?

DOROTHY: I'm pretty well, thank you. How do you do?

SCARECROW: I'm not feeling well. It's very tedious being perched up here night and day to scare away crows. If you will help me down, I shall be greatly obliged to you. (DOROTHY *helps him down.*) Thank you very much. Who are you, and where are you going?

DOROTHY: My name is Dorothy, and I am going to the Emerald City to ask the great Oz to send me back to Kansas.

SCARECROW: Who is Oz?

DOROTHY: Why, don't you know?

SCARECROW: No, I am stuffed and have no brain.

DOROTHY: Oh, I'm sorry. Emerald City is the place we need to go to see Oz, the wizard.

SCARECROW: Do you suppose that if I go with you, that Oz would give me some brains?

DOROTHY: I cannot tell, but come if you like.

SCARECROW: I think I shall. (DOROTHY *and the* SCARECROW *walk around the stage. They walk by the* TIN WOODMAN.)

DOROTHY: I'm sure I heard someone groan. *(Looks at* TIN WOODMAN)

TIN WOODMAN: Yes, you heard me groan.

DOROTHY: What can I do for you?

TIN WOODMAN: Get an oilcan and oil my joints. They are rusted so badly that I cannot move them at all.

DOROTHY: Very well. (DOROTHY *gets the oilcan and begins to oil.)*

TIN WOODMAN: Oh, it is wonderful to move again! How did you happen to be here?

DOROTHY: We are on our way to the Emerald City to see the Great Oz. I want him to send me back to Kansas.

TIN WOODMAN: Do you suppose Oz could give me a heart?

DOROTHY: Why, I guess so. It would be as easy as giving the Scarecrow brains.

SCARECROW: Come along! Pleased to have you.

TIN WOODMAN: Look! A lion!

COWARDLY LION: Roar! Roar! (LION *runs after everyone and tries to bite* TOTO.)

DOROTHY: Don't you dare to bite Toto! You ought to be ashamed of yourself. You're a beast and nothing but a big coward.

LION: I know that I'm a coward. All the other animals in the forest naturally expect me to be brave. I know that if I roar very loudly, the other animals are terrified and get out of my way.

SCARECROW: A lion should not be a coward.

LION: I know it, and it makes me very unhappy. What are you doing here?

DOROTHY: We are going to the Great Oz to ask him for help.

LION: Do you think Oz could give me courage?

DOROTHY: Yes, it would be just as easy for him to help you as it would be to help us.

LION: Then I'll go with you, for my life is unbearable without courage.

DOROTHY: You are very welcome to join us on our long journey to the Emerald City.

Answer these questions.

1. Where was Dorothy after her house stopped whirling?

2. What happened to the Wicked Witch of the East?

3. Why did Dorothy want to see the Great Oz?

4. Who did Dorothy meet along the way to the Emerald City?

5. Why did the Witch of the North give the silver shoes to Dorothy?

The Wizard of Oz

Oz, the Great and Terrible

TIME: *A few days later.*

SETTING: *Outside of* OZ'*s throne room.*

DOROTHY: I am so glad to be here. I thought we
would never arrive.

TIN WOODMAN: Let us hope that the great Oz will
see us. *(The* CAPTAIN *walks on stage.)*

DOROTHY: Have you asked Oz about us?

CAPTAIN: I gave him your message. When I mentioned your silver shoes, he said he would grant you an audience. But each of you must enter his presence alone.

DOROTHY: Thank you. It is very kind of Oz to see us.

SETTING: *The throne room.*

OZ: I am Oz, the Great and Terrible. Who are you, and why do you seek me?

DOROTHY: I am Dorothy and I have come for help.

OZ: Where did you get the silver shoes?

DOROTHY: I got them from the Wicked Witch of the East when my house fell on her.

OZ: What do you wish me to do?

DOROTHY: Send me back to Kansas to my aunt Em and my uncle Henry.

OZ: I will not grant you a favor unless you do something for me in return. Kill the Wicked Witch of the West. She is a tremendously cruel witch.

DOROTHY: I cannot! I never killed anything, willingly, and even if I wanted to, how could I kill the Wicked Witch? If you cannot kill her, how do you expect me to?

OZ: I do not know, but until the Wicked Witch of the West is dead, you will not see Kansas again. (DOROTHY *leaves the throne room and the* SCARECROW *enters.*)

OZ: I am Oz, the Great and Terrible. Who are you, and why do you seek me?

SCARECROW: I am only a Scarecrow, stuffed with straw, and I have no brains. I want you to give me brains so I may be like a man.

OZ: I never grant a favor without some return. If you will kill the Wicked Witch of the West for me, I will give you brains. Go and do not seek me again until you have earned the brains you so greatly desire. (SCARECROW *leaves and the* TIN WOODMAN *enters.)*

OZ: I am Oz, the Great and Terrible. Who are you, and why do you seek me?

TIN WOODMAN: I am the Tin Woodman, and I have no heart and cannot love. I ask you to give me a heart.

OZ: If you indeed desire a heart, you must earn it.

TIN WOODMAN: How?

OZ: Help kill the Wicked Witch of the West. When she is dead, come and I will then give you the most loving heart in the land. *(The* TIN WOOD-MAN *leaves the throne room and the* LION *enters.)*

OZ: I am Oz, the Great and Terrible. Who are you, and why do you seek me?

LION: I am a Cowardly Lion, though I am supposed to be King of the Beasts. I have come to you to ask for courage.

OZ: I will grant you courage only if you will help kill the Wicked Witch of the West.

LION: But how can a coward like me do that?

OZ: I do not know, but after she is dead, you may come back and I will make you the most courageous beast in all the forest.

NARRATOR: The next morning the four friends started for the castle of the Wicked Witch of the West. Now, the Wicked Witch of the West had a very powerful eye that could see everywhere. As she stood in front of her castle, she looked out and saw Dorothy with her friends. She was furious to find them in her country, and tried many ways to capture them, but was unsuccessful. Then the powerful witch had one last idea.

SETTING: *In front of the castle of the* WICKED WITCH OF THE WEST.

WICKED WITCH: The only way left to destroy the strangers is with the Golden Cap. This must be my last command to the Winged Monkeys. *(She says the chant.)* Ep-pe, pep-pe, kak-ke! Hil-lo, hol-lo, hel-lo! Ziz-zy, zuz-zy, zik! *(The* KING OF THE MONKEYS *enters.)*

KING OF THE MONKEYS: You have called us for the
last time. What do you command?

WICKED WITCH: Go to the strangers within my
land and destroy all of them except the Lion.
Bring that beast to me, for I shall harness him
and make him work like a horse.

KING OF THE MONKEYS: Your commands shall be
obeyed.

NARRATOR: The Monkeys flew to Dorothy and her friends. First they threw the Tin Woodman in a valley covered with sharp rocks, where he lay battered and dented. Then they caught the Scarecrow and pulled the straw out of his clothes.

KING OF THE MONKEYS: We have obeyed you. We dare not harm the little girl or the dog she carries with her, for the Witch of the North is protecting her. Your power over our band is now ended. *(The* KING OF THE MONKEYS *exits.* DOROTHY *comes in.)*

WICKED WITCH: Dorothy! At last I have you.

DOROTHY: You are a very wicked witch for destroying my friends and tying up the Lion, but your power cannot last long. I have a special charm in my silver shoes and it will help me to get rid of you.

WICKED WITCH: The silver shoes! Give them to me!

DOROTHY: No! *(The* WITCH *and* DOROTHY *struggle over the shoes. The* WITCH *gets one shoe.)*

WICKED WITCH: There! Now I have your shoe and your charm will be useless.

DOROTHY: You wicked creature! You have no right to take my shoe from me.

WICKED WITCH: I shall keep it, and someday I shall get the other one from you, too.

DOROTHY: Oh! (DOROTHY *seizes a bucket of water and dashes it over the* WICKED WITCH, *who begins to shrink.*)

WICKED WITCH: See what you have done? In a minute I shall melt away.

DOROTHY: I'm very sorry, indeed.

WICKED WITCH: Didn't you know water would be the end of me?

DOROTHY: Of course not. How could I?

WICKED WITCH: Well, in a minute I shall be all melted, and you will have the castle to yourself. You have ended my wicked deeds. (*The* WICKED WITCH *melts away.*)

DOROTHY: I may as well get her out of here. And take my shoe, too. Perhaps I shall take her Golden Cap also. It fits! Now I must go back to the Emerald City for my reward. But how can I save the Scarecrow and the Tin Woodman and the Lion? What can I do? Oh, look! There's a magic rhyme in the cap! Maybe it will help me. (DOROTHY *reads the rhyme.*) Ep-pe, pep-pe, kak-ke! Hil-lo, hol-lo, hel-lo! Ziz-zy, zuz-zy, zik! *(The* KING OF THE MONKEYS *enters.)*

KING OF THE MONKEYS: What is your command? We can take you anywhere within the Land of Oz.

DOROTHY: I wish to go to the Emerald City, but I must rescue my friends first.

KING OF THE MONKEYS: We will carry you there, and we will find your friends. Have no fear.

Answer these questions.

1. Why did Oz agree to see Dorothy and her friends when the Captain mentioned the silver shoes?

2. What did the Wizard ask Dorothy and her friends to do?

3. Why couldn't the Monkeys hurt Dorothy and her dog?

4. What happened when Dorothy threw water on the Wicked Witch?

5. Where did Dorothy command the King of the Monkeys to take her and her friends?

The Wizard of Oz

Back to the Emerald City

SETTING: Oz's *throne room.*

DOROTHY: That was a good ride.

LION: Yes, how lucky it was that you took that wonderful cap, Dorothy.

DOROTHY: I wonder where Oz is. I don't see anyone.

OZ *(From behind a screen):* I am Oz, the Great and Terrible. Why do you seek me?

DOROTHY: We have come to claim our rewards.

OZ: What rewards?

DOROTHY: You promised to grant us all our wishes when the Wicked Witch was destroyed.

OZ: Is she really destroyed?

DOROTHY: Yes, I melted her with a bucket of water.

OZ: My, how sudden! Well, come to me tomorrow, for I must have time to think it over.

DOROTHY: You've had plenty of time already. You must keep your promises to us. (LION *roars loudly, and* DOROTHY *jumps and drops* TOTO. TOTO *runs and knocks over the screen, revealing a little old man.)*

TIN WOODMAN: Who are you?

OZ: I am Oz, the Great and Terrible, but—but—
I'll do anything you want me to.

DOROTHY: You are Oz?

OZ: I am, but I have been making believe. I'm supposed to be a Great Wizard, but I'm just a com-
mon man.

SCARECROW: You're a fake!

OZ: Exactly! But don't speak so loudly. If someone hears you, I shall be ruined.

DOROTHY: But this is terrible. How shall we ever
get the rewards you promised?

Oz: My friends, think of me, and the terrible trouble I'm in since you found me out.

SCARECROW: Really, you ought to be ashamed of yourself for being such a fake.

Oz: I am, but being a fake was the only thing I could do. You see, one day I went up in a balloon and I couldn't come down again. I floated miles through the air until I landed here. The people here thought I was a Great Wizard, and I have been good to them. But one of my greatest fears was the Witches. That is why I would promise anything if you would do away with the other Witch. But I am ashamed to say now that I cannot keep my promises.

DOROTHY: I think you are a very bad man.

Oz: Oh, no, my dear. I'm really a very good man, but I must admit I'm a very bad Wizard.

SCARECROW: Can't you give me brains?

Oz: You don't need them. You are learning every day. Experience brings knowledge, and the longer you live, the more you will learn.

SCARECROW: That may all be true, but I shall be very unhappy unless I have brains.

Oz: Then I will try to give you brains. I cannot tell you how to use them, however; you must find that out for yourself.

SCARECROW: Oh, thank you, thank you. And I'll
find a way to use them, never fear.

LION: Now, how about my courage?

OZ: All you need is to have confidence in yourself. True courage is facing danger when you
are afraid, and you have plenty of true
courage.

LION: Maybe I have, but I'm scared anyway.

OZ: Very well, I will get some courage for you.
(Holds up glass) Drink this.

LION: What is it?

OZ: Well, if it were inside of you, it would be
courage. Now swallow it.

TIN WOODMAN: How about my heart?

OZ: Why, I think you are wrong to want a heart.
It makes most people unhappy.

TIN WOODMAN: I will bear all the unhappiness if you will give me a heart.

OZ: Very well. *(Holds up paper heart)* Isn't it beautiful? It is a heart to be proud of.

TIN WOODMAN: Yes, it is.

DOROTHY: And how am I to get back to Kansas?

OZ: I'll have to think about that for a while.

NARRATOR: Oz finally decided that he and Dorothy should leave in a balloon, but at the moment they were to take off, Dorothy could not locate Toto. By the time she found him, the balloon was already sailing overhead, and Oz could not bring it back. She was very sad, and cried because she thought she would never get back to Kansas. Finally Dorothy found out that Glinda, the Good Witch of the South, might help her.

TIME: *A few days later.*

SETTING: *A room in* GLINDA'*s castle.*

DOROTHY: This must be Glinda's castle.

GLINDA: I am Glinda, the Good Witch of the South. What can I do for you?

DOROTHY: My greatest wish is to get back to Kansas to my aunt and uncle.

GLINDA: I am sure I can help you. But if I do, you must give me the Golden Cap.

DOROTHY: Of course. It's of no use to me now.

GLINDA: I think I will need it just three times. Scarecrow, what will you do when Dorothy has left us?

SCARECROW: I will return to the Emerald City, for Oz has made me its ruler. What worries me is how I will cross the tremendous mountain bordering your land.

GLINDA: By the Golden Cap I shall command the Winged Monkeys to carry you again to the Emerald City, for we mustn't deprive the people of a wonderful ruler. Tin Woodman, what will become of you?

TIN WOODMAN: The Winkies in the land of the West were very kind to me and wanted me to rule over them. If I could get back again, I should like nothing better than to be their ruler forever.

GLINDA: My second command to the Winged Monkeys is that they carry you safely to the land of the Winkies. Lion, when Dorothy has gone home, what will become of you?

LION: The beasts in the forest of your land have made me their king. If I could get back to them, I would enjoy a happy life.

GLINDA: My third command to the Winged Monkeys is to carry you to your forest. Then, having used up the powers of the Golden Cap, I shall give it to the King of the Monkeys, so that he and his band may be free forever.

SCARECROW, TIN WOODMAN, LION: Thank you.

DOROTHY: You are very kind. But you have not yet told me how to get back to Kansas.

GLINDA: Your silver shoes have wonderful powers. If you had known their power, you could have gone back to your aunt Em the very first day you came to this country. All you have to do is knock your heels together three times and command the shoes to carry you wherever you wish.

DOROTHY: I shall command them at once. Goodbye, my friends. I'll never forget you.

SCARECROW, TIN WOODMAN, LION: Goodbye, Dorothy. We shall always remember you, too.

DOROTHY *(Knocking her heels together three times):* Take me home to Aunt Em! Good gracious, here I am in Kansas!

AUNT EM: My darling child! Where in the world have you been?

DOROTHY: In the Land of Oz. And here's Toto. Oh, Aunt Em, I'm so glad to be at home again.

Answer these questions.

1. What did Dorothy and her friends see when Toto knocked over the screen?

2. How did Oz plan to get Dorothy back to Kansas?

3. What was the Scarecrow going to do after Dorothy went back to Kansas?

4. Why was Oz's greatest fear the witches?

About the Author

   L. Frank Baum wrote children's books about the imaginary country of Oz. *The Wonderful Wizard of Oz,* his most popular book, became a musical comedy in 1901 and a movie in 1939. He was born in Chittenango, New York.

STORMS

Keiko Watanabe

Who doesn't like to talk about the weather? It is important to all of us, and storms are an important part of weather. Storms can produce hard rain, blowing snow, large hail, or damaging winds.

One kind of storm is a blizzard. It is a heavy snowstorm with very strong winds that whip the snow around so hard and fast it can be blinding. A blizzard happens in the winter, when very cold air from the Arctic flows south and meets warmer air in the Midwest, causing clouds to form and a blizzard to start.

Because of the blowing snow, a blizzard makes it difficult for people to drive or walk anywhere. And since it is usually very cold during a blizzard, keeping safe and warm is important, so people try to stay indoors.

Another storm is the hurricane, which starts over the ocean. The winds get faster and rain clouds form. The hurricane grows, and then it moves over the land, bringing strong winds and heavy rains. The entire storm can be hundreds of miles wide and can last days or weeks. But it always keeps moving on to new areas, until finally it gets weaker and disappears.

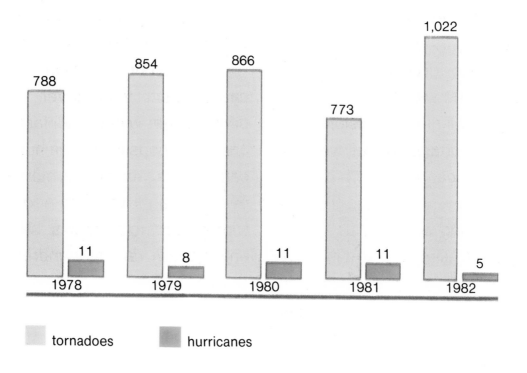

788 1978
854 1979
866 1980
773 1981
1,022 1982

11 8 11 11 5

tornadoes   hurricanes

Hurricanes form between June and December, but they occur most often in September. They usually occur along the Atlantic Coast or in the Gulf of Mexico.

In hurricane season, the weather service keeps a close watch. If a storm starts, warnings are sent out so that people in the area can go indoors or leave town, waiting for the storm to pass.

The hurricane also gets a name. The first storm of the year gets a person's name that starts with the letter A. The second storm gets the letter B. Each storm that year gets a name beginning with a new letter of the alphabet.

One of the strongest windstorms of all is the tornado. It typically starts on a hot, sticky, cloudy afternoon.

The tornado forms when dry air from the north meets wet air from the south, causing dark clouds to form. The dark clouds start to change at the bottom, and a funnellike shape forms. This funnel grows until it reaches the ground, and then it starts to travel, roaring as it goes. This storm is sometimes called a twister, because the winds blow in a tight circle and the funnel seems to twist around.

Tornadoes hit mostly in the Midwest, but they can also occur in other areas of the country. Usually tornadoes occur in the spring or the summer. The storm usually does not last long, and the funnel soon disappears or moves on. Some people stay in a storm cellar; everybody waits until the storm is over.

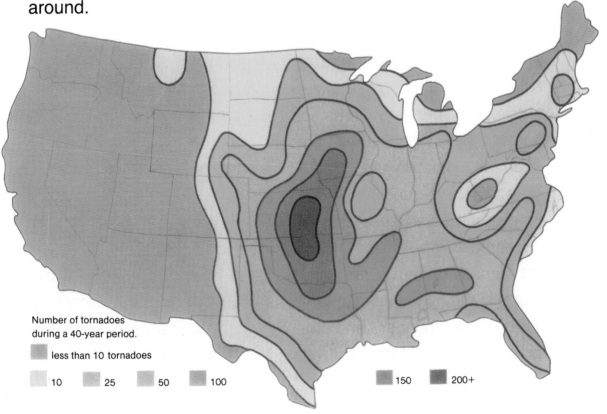

Number of tornadoes during a 40-year period.

less than 10 tornadoes

10   25   50   100   150   200+

There are other types of storms, too, which add beauty and excitement to our lives. A snowstorm brings billions of snowflakes. When they are examined, no two are exactly alike. Each tiny snowflake has its own shape and beauty.

Almost everyone has awakened during a thunderstorm in the middle of the night. The noisy thunder and the bright lightning startle and excite spectators.

There are gentle rainstorms, too. When people hear the soft sounds of quiet, falling rain, they often feel peaceful. Sometimes after it rains a beautiful rainbow appears in the sky as an enormous arch of colored stripes.

There are many kinds of storms, some of which cause extreme kinds of weather. Others bring a simple beauty to us. Storms of all kinds are a part of our lives.

Answer these questions.

1. What do the strong winds of a blizzard do?

2. Where does a hurricane start?

3. Why is a tornado sometimes called a twister?

4. What sometimes happens after it rains?

5. Why is it important to know about storms?

Write on your own.

Pretend you have recently experienced a storm. Write five sentences telling what you saw and heard.

Open Range

Prairie goes to the mountain,
    Mountain goes to the sky.
The sky sweeps across to the distant hills
And here, in the middle,
    Am I.

Hills crowd down to the river,
    River runs by the tree.
Tree throws its shadow on sunburnt grass
And here, in the shadow,
    Is me.

Shadows creep up the mountain,
    Mountain goes black on the sky,
The sky bursts out with a million stars
And here, by the campfire,
    Am I.

Kathryn and Byron Jackson

Words to Know for Safety

We should all be concerned about our safety and the safety of those around us. These are words that will help keep us safe.

Construction zone   Pedestrians prohibited
Fire extinguisher   Not for internal use
No admittance   Condemned
Combustible   Storm shelter

Number your paper from 1 to 8. Read each of these sentences and write the correct words beside the number of the sentence.

1. You should not be walking here.

2. People are not allowed to enter.

3. You should go here if a tornado is sighted.

4. This place is not fit to live in.

5. Please do not swallow this.

6. This will burn easily.

7. This should be used to stop something from burning.

8. Something is being built here.

A Bear Called Paddington

Michael Bond

Paddington soon settled down and became one of the family. The Browns lived near the Portobello Road, where there was a big market, and quite often, when Mrs. Brown was busy, she let him go out to do the shopping for her.

Now Paddington spent a lot of his time looking in shop windows, and of all the windows in the Portobello Road, Mr. Gruber's was the best. It was full of interesting things. Old pieces of furniture, medals, pots and pans, pictures; there were so many things it was difficult to get inside the shop, and old Mr. Gruber spent a lot of his time sitting in a deckchair on the pavement. Mr. Gruber, in his turn, found Paddington very interesting and soon they had become great friends. Paddington often stopped there on his way home from a shopping expedition.

Mr. Gruber always called Paddington 'Mr. Brown,' and it made him feel very important.

"Things aren't always what they seem in this world, Mr. Brown," he said, sadly.

Paddington sighed. It was very disappointing. "I wish they were," he said. "It would be so nice."

"Perhaps," said Mr. Gruber mysteriously. "Perhaps. But we shouldn't have any nice surprises then, should we?"

He took Paddington into his shop and after offering him a seat disappeared for a moment. When he returned he was carrying a large picture of a boat. At least, half of it was a boat. The other half seemed to be the picture of a lady in a large hat.

"There you are," he said, proudly. "That's what I mean by things not always being what they seem. I'd like your opinion on it, Mr. Brown."

Paddington felt rather flattered but also puzzled. The picture didn't seem to be one thing or the other and he said so.

"Ah," said Mr. Gruber, delightedly. "It isn't at the moment. When I started to clean it the other day all the paint began to come off and I discovered there was another painting underneath." He looked around and then lowered his voice. "Nobody else knows," he whispered, "but I think the one underneath may be valuable. It may be what they call an 'old master.' "

Seeing that Paddington still looked puzzled, he explained to him that in the old days, when artists ran short of money and couldn't afford any canvas to paint on, they sometimes painted on top of old pictures. And sometimes, very occasionally, they painted on top of pictures by artists who afterwards became famous and whose pictures were worth a lot of money. But as they had been painted over, no one knew anything about them.

Mr. Gruber talked for a long time about painting, which was one of his favorite subjects. But Paddington, though he was usually interested in anything Mr. Gruber had to tell him, was hardly listening. Paddington had an idea.

When he got home he went upstairs to his room and lay on the bed for a long while, staring up at the ceiling. He was up there so long that Mrs. Bird became quite worried and poked her head round the door to know if he was all right.

"Quite all right, thank you," said Paddington, distantly. "I'm just thinking."

Mrs. Bird closed the door and hurried downstairs to tell the others. "I don't mind him *just* thinking," said Mrs. Brown, with a worried expression on her face. "It's when he actually thinks *of* something that the trouble starts."

But she was in the middle of her work and soon forgot the matter. Certainly both she and Mrs. Bird were much too busy to notice the small figure of a bear creeping cautiously in the direction of Mr. Brown's shed a few minutes later. Nor did they see him return armed with a bottle of Mr. Brown's paint remover and a large pile of rags. And if Mrs. Brown had seen him creeping on tiptoe into the drawing-room, closing the door carefully behind him, she wouldn't have had a minute's peace.

Fortunately everyone was much too busy to notice any of these things. Even more fortunately, no one came into the drawing-room for quite a long while. Because Paddington was in a mess. Things hadn't gone at all according to plan. He was beginning to wish he had listened more carefully to the things Mr. Gruber had said on the subject of cleaning paintings.

To start with, even though he'd used almost half a bottle of Mr. Brown's paint remover, the picture had only come off in patches. Secondly, and what was even worse, where it *had* come off there was nothing underneath. Only the white canvas. Paddington stood back and surveyed his handiwork. Originally it had been a painting of a lake, with a blue sky and several sailing boats dotted around. Now it looked like a storm at sea. All the boats had gone, the sky was a funny shade of grey, and half the lake had disappeared.

"What a good thing I found this old box of paints," he thought. Holding a palette in his left paw, he squeezed some red paint on to it and then splodged it about with the brush. He looked nervously over his shoulder and then dabbed some of it on to the canvas.

He wiped the brush carefully on his hat and tried another colour and then another. He very soon forgot the fact that he was supposed to be painting a picture.

In fact, it was more of a design than a picture, with lines and circles and crosses all in different colours. Even Paddington was startled when he finally stepped back to examine it. Of the original picture there was no trace at all. Rather sadly he put the tubes of paint back into the box and wrapped the

picture in a canvas bag, leaning it against the wall, exactly as he'd found it. He decided reluctantly to have another try later on.

He was so silent through dinner that evening that several times Mrs. Brown asked him how he was, until eventually Paddington asked to be excused and went upstairs.

"He hardly touched his dinner and that's so unlike him," she said after he'd gone. "And he seemed to have some red spots all over his face."

"Crikey," said Jonathan. "Red spots! I hope he's given it to me, whatever it is, then I shan't have to go back to school!"

"Well, he's got green ones as well," said Judy.

"Green ones!" Even Mr. Brown looked worried. "I wonder if he's sickening for anything? If they're not gone in the morning I'll send for the doctor."

"He was so looking forward to going to the handicrafts exhibition, too," said Mrs. Brown.

"Do you think you'll win a prize with your painting, Dad?" asked Jonathan.

"What is it, Daddy?" asked Judy. "Aren't you going to tell us?"

"It's meant to be a surprise," said Mr. Brown modestly. "It took me a long time to do. It's painted from memory."

Painting was one of Mr. Brown's hobbies, and once a year he entered a picture for a handicrafts exhibition. Several famous people came to judge the pictures and there were a number of prizes.

"Anyway," he said, declaring the subject closed, "it's too late now. The man collected it this afternoon, so we shall see what we shall see."

The sun was shining the next day and the exhibition was crowded. Everyone was pleased that Paddington looked so much better. His spots had completely disappeared and he ate a large breakfast to make up for missing so much dinner the night before. Only Mrs. Bird had her suspicions when she found Paddington's 'spots' on his towel in the bathroom, but she kept her thoughts to herself.

There was an air of great excitement. It was news to Paddington that Mr. Brown actually painted and he was looking forward to seeing a picture by someone he knew.

On the platform several important-looking men were bustling about talking to each other and waving their arms in the air. They appeared to be having a great deal of argument about one painting in particular.

"Henry," whispered Mrs. Brown, excitedly. "I do believe they're talking about your painting. I recognise the canvas bag."

Mr. Brown looked puzzled. "It certainly looks like my bag," he said. "But I don't think it can be. All the canvas was stuck to the painting. Didn't you see? Just as if someone had put it inside while it was still wet. I painted mine ages ago."

Paddington sat very still and stared straight ahead, hardly daring to move. He had a strange sinking feeling in the bottom of his stomach, as if something awful were about to happen. He began to wish he hadn't washed his spots off that morning; then at least he could have stayed in bed.

Judy poked him with her elbow. "Paddington," she asked, "you look most peculiar. Are you all right?"

"I don't feel ill," said Paddington in a small voice. "But I think I'm in trouble again."

Paddington sat up. One of the men on the platform was speaking. And there . . . Paddington's knees began to tremble . . . there, on the platform, on an easel in full view of everyone, was 'his' picture!

He was so dazed he only caught scraps of what the man was saying.

". . . remarkable use of colour . . ."

". . . very unusual . . ."

". . . great imagination . . . a credit to the artist . . ."

And then, he almost fell off his seat with surprise.

"The winner of the first prize is Mr. Henry Brown of thirty-two Windsor Gardens!"

Paddington wasn't the only one who felt surprised. Mr. Brown, who was being helped up on to the platform, looked as if he had just been struck by lightning. "But . . . but . . ." he stuttered, "there must be some mistake."

"Mistake?" said the man. "Nonsense, my dear sir. Your name's on the back of the canvas. You *are* Mr. Brown, aren't you? Mr. *Henry* Brown?"

Mr. Brown looked at the painting with unbelieving eyes. "It's certainly my name on the back," he said. "It's my writing . . ." He left the sentence unfinished and looked down towards the audience. He had his own ideas on the subject, but it was difficult to catch Paddington's eye. It usually was when you particularly wanted to.

"I think," said Mr. Brown, when the applause had died down and he had accepted the cheque for ten pounds which the man gave him, "proud as I am, I think I would like to donate the prize to a certain home for retired bears in South America." Paddington was staring hard at the painting, and in particular at the man on the platform, who was beginning to look hot and bothered.

"I think," said Paddington, to the world in general, "they might have stood it the right way up. It's not every day a bear wins first prize in a painting competition!"

Answer these questions.

1. What was Mr. Gruber doing to the picture of the boat?

2. What did the painting look like after Paddington tried to clean it?

3. What does the phrase "to catch someone's eye" mean?

4. To what did Mr. Brown donate his prize?

Write on your own.

Pretend that you are Paddington. You are writing a letter to the home for retired bears in South America to explain about the money they are receiving. Make the letter about seven sentences long.

Words to Know on Airplanes

Have you ever flown on an airplane? Have you ever gone to an airport to meet someone or to see someone off on a trip? You may have seen these words in an airport or on an airplane.

Fasten seat belts   Oxygen
Emergency exit   Arrival
Baggage claim   No smoking
Information   Departure

Write the word **airplane** on one side of your paper and the word **airport** on the other side. Write the words under the place you think you would see them. Some of the words may be seen in both places.

Number your paper from 1 to 8. Write the correct answer from the list of words.

1. Where would you go to get your questions answered?
2. Which sign tells you which planes are coming in?
3. Where would you go to pick up your suitcases?
4. What would you do to protect yourself on an airplane?
5. Which word names something that is necessary to live?
6. What sign tells adults not to do something?
7. Which sign tells you which planes are leaving?
8. Where would you go to get out of the plane quickly?

Vocabulary Review

Read each sentence and the four answers that follow it. Decide which answer best completes the sentence. Write the answer on your paper.

1. To have courage is to be _____.
   a. courteous
   b. energetic
   c. brave
   d. patient

2. A person who is cruel to others is _____.
   a. crooked
   b. thoughtful
   c. anxious
   d. mean

3. If something is fake, it is _____.
   a. not real
   b. not beautiful
   c. very kind
   d. very faded

4. Spectators are the _____ who watch football games.
   a. tourists
   b. people
   c. workers
   d. participants

5. To act in a peculiar way is to act _____.
   a. freely
   b. strangely
   c. slowly
   d. swiftly

Books to Read

Erickson, Russell E.   *A Toad for Tuesday*

A toad named Warton sets out on a dangerous winter journey to deliver beetle brittle to his aunt. Injured from a fall and captured by an owl who plans to eat him in five days, he plots his escape.

Graves, Charles P.   *The Wright Brothers*

Because of a toy, Wilbur and Orville Wright become interested in flying machines while they are young children. They invent several things and improve several inventions as they grow up, but their struggle to build the first successful airplane results in their most famous accomplishment.

Hawkinson, John   *Collect, Print, and Paint Nature*

By looking carefully at nature's items from the woods, the city, the beach, and other places, and by following simple instructions, you can use your memory and imagination to make prints or paint pictures.

Livingston, Myra Cohn   *Sky Songs*

Paintings and poems reflect the moods and changes in the sky caused by shifts in the time of day and various weather conditions.

Glossary

Entries adapted from *The HBJ School Dictionary*, copyright © 1977, 1972, 1968 by Harcourt Brace Jovanovich, Inc., are reprinted by permission of the publisher.

Key to Pronunciation
Listed below are diacritical symbols and key words. The boldface letters in the key words represent the sounds indicated by the symbols.

/ā/	c**a**ke	/d/	**d**uck
/ă/	h**a**t	/ē/	b**ea**n
/ä/	f**a**ther	/ĕ/	p**e**t
/är/	c**ar**	/f/	**f**un
/âr/	c**are**	/g/	**g**o
/b/	**b**oy	/gz/	e**x**act
/ch/	**ch**urch	/h/	**h**ome
/(h)w/	**wh**ite	/ou/	**ou**t
/ī/	p**ie**	/p/	**p**et
/ĭ/	p**i**g	/r/	**r**un
/ir/	d**ear**	/s/	**s**ee
/j/	**j**ump	/sh/	**sh**ip
/k/	**k**ite	/t/	**t**op
/ks/	bo**x**	/th/	**th**in
/kw/	**qu**it	/t̵h/	**th**is
/l/	**l**ook	/ŭ/	n**u**t
/m/	**m**an	/ûr/	f**ur**
/n/	**n**ot	/v/	**v**ine
/ng/	si**ng**	/w/	**w**ill
/ō/	r**o**pe	/y/	**y**es
/ŏ/	t**o**p	/yo͞o/	**u**se
/ô/	s**aw**	/z/	**z**oo
/oi/	**oi**l	/zh/	a**z**ure
/o͞o/	m**oo**n	/ə/	**a**bove
/o͝o/	b**oo**k		**circus**
/ôr/	f**or**k	/ər/	bitt**er**

A a

ac·tor [ăk′tər] **ac·tors** Person or persons who perform in movies or plays: The *actors* made the play a success.

am·bi·tion [ăm·bĭsh′ən] An eager desire to succeed or to achieve a goal: The boy's great *ambition* was to become a football star.

an·kle [ăng′kəl] **an·kles** The joint connecting the foot and the leg: She stumbled over the box and broke her *ankle*.

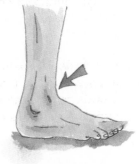

arch [ärch] A curved structure: An *arch* is often used to support a bridge.

Ar·gen·ti·na [är′jən·tē′nə] A country in southern South America: The capital of *Argentina* is Buenos Aires.

ar·gu·ment [är′gyə·mənt] An angry discussion: The two children had an *argument* over who saw the dollar first.

ar·range·ment [ə·rānj′mənt] A plan or set of plans: The pupils liked the new *arrangement* of moving from classroom to classroom.

330

ar·ti·fact [är′tə·făkt] **ar·ti·facts** Anything made by the work of people: We know more about the early Egyptians by looking at their tools and other *artifacts*.

au·di·ence [ô′dē·əns] A group of listeners or watchers: The *audience* laughed at the speaker's jokes.

ax·el [ăk′səl] A jump in figure skating consisting of one and a half turns in the air: The skater ended the program with a graceful *axel*.

B b

bal·ance [băl′əns] The ability to keep one's body in a certain position without falling: Tightrope walkers must keep their *balance* or they will fall.

bam·boo [băm·bōo] A tall, treelike tropical grass with hollow stems: The *bamboo* tree can be used to make furniture.

bat·ter [băt′ər] **bat·tered** Damaged by hard blows: The waves *battered* the boat and almost destroyed it.

blast [blăst] A strong wind or rush of air: A *blast* of cold air rushed in through the open window.

bliz·zard [blĭz′ərd] A very heavy snowstorm: The *blizzard* made driving very difficult for motorists.

boom·er [bōōm′ər] A person who travels around from job to job: When the *boomer* finished building the bridge, he moved on.

buck·le [bŭk′əl] **buckling** To bend or twist: The fawn's legs were *buckling* underneath it as it tried to stand.

bunt [bŭnt] To bat a ball very lightly and low: The baseball player plans to *bunt* the ball and run.

C c

cab [kăb] An enclosed compartment in a train for the use of an operator: The engineer rode in the *cab* in the front of the train.

can·vas [kăn′vəs] A heavy cloth on which an artist can paint: The artist chose a new *canvas* for the portrait.

cast [kăst] To cause to fall upon, such as to *cast* a shadow: When clouds move between us and the sun, a shadow is *cast* over us.

cel·e·brate [sĕl′ə·brāt] To observe or honor: We like to *celebrate* the beginning of a new year.

cer·e·mo·ni·al [sĕr′ə·mō′nē·əl] Used in a ceremony: The *ceremonial* jewels were kept in the safe.

cer·e·mo·ny [sĕr′ə·mō′nē] **cer·e·mo·nies** Any formal act performed in a set way: They received their awards in special *ceremonies*.

cham·pi·on [chăm′pē·ən] 1. A person who comes out ahead of all others in a competition. 2. Anything awarded first place: The *champion* swimmer received a gold medal.

chan·nel [chăn′əl] A body of water that connects two other bodies of water: We crossed the *channel* to the island yesterday.

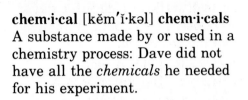

chem·i·cal [kĕm′ĭ·kəl] **chem·i·cals** A substance made by or used in a chemistry process: Dave did not have all the *chemicals* he needed for his experiment.

chem·is·try [kĕm′ĭs·trē] The science that deals with substances and the ways in which they interact: *Chemistry* experiments can help us learn more about the world around us.

Cher·o·kee [chĕr′ə·kē] A member of an Indian tribe, which now lives mainly in Oklahoma: The *Cherokee* Indians once lived in Georgia and North Carolina.

chief [chēf] **chiefs** The leader of a tribe or of a group, such as the police force: The old *chief* gathered all the braves together.

claim [klām] To demand what belongs to oneself: I will *claim* the prize tomorrow.

clus·ter [klŭs′tər] A group of things that are alike: The bear crashed through the *cluster* of bushes.

coal [kōl] A black or dark mineral, which gives off heat when burned: *Coal* is formed when decayed plants are put under great pressure.

coax [kōks] **coax·ing** To ask or persuade in a gentle and flattering way: She tried *coaxing* her puppy with a dog biscuit.

col·lect [kə·lĕkt′] **col·lect·ed** To gather things together: The papers were *collected* after the test.

com·mand [kə·mănd′] 1. To be in control of. 2. An order: The captain gave a *command* to the crew.

com·mo·tion [kə·mō′shən] Confusion, excitement, or disturbance: The children heard the *commotion* on the playground.

com·mu·ni·cate [kə·myo͞o′nə·kāt] To give or exchange thoughts, information, or messages: Letters are a good way to *communicate*.

com·plaint [kəm·plānt′] The thing complained about: He listened closely to their *complaint* about the toy that broke soon after it was bought.

com·pli·cate [kŏm′plə·kāt] **com·pli·cat·ed** To make or become hard to understand, use, solve: This game seems *complicated* to me, so let's find one that's easier.

com·pli·ment [kŏm′plə·mənt] **com·pli·ments** An expression of admiration or praise: I received many *compliments* on my speech.

con·ceal [kən·sēl′] **con·cealed** To keep secret or hidden: The hunter *concealed* himself behind the log so that he wouldn't be seen.

con·cerned [kən·sûrnd′] 1. Interested. 2. Uneasy or worried: Mrs. Brown became *concerned* when you were absent.

con·fi·dence [kŏn′fə·dəns] A feeling of trust in oneself or others: The coach had *confidence* in the team's ability to win.

con·fi·dent [kŏn′fə·dənt] Having confidence or being assured: He was *confident* he would win the race.

con·fuse [kən·fyo͞oz′] **con·fused** To be mixed up or to be perplexed: I think that you are lost because you are *confused* about the directions.

con·ver·sa·tion [kŏn′vər·sā′shən] An exchange of ideas through talk: I had an interesting *conversation* with the teacher about her hobby.

con·vince [kən·vĭns′] **con·vinced** Feeling certain: She was *convinced* that she was right.

coun·cil [koun′səl] A group of people meeting to discuss and plan: The city *council* voted to buy a new fire truck.

cour·age [kûr′ij] Bravery; ability to meet danger in spite of fear: An acrobat must have *courage* to walk on a tightrope.

cow·ard·ly [kou′ərd·lē] Being without courage: He admitted he had been *cowardly* when he ran away.

cru·el [kro͞o′əl] Brutal; to give pain to others: People should not be *cruel* to each other.

cu·ri·os·i·ty [kyo͞or′ē·ŏs′ə·tē] A great desire to know or to find out: It takes a lot of *curiosity* to be a good scientist.

cus·to·di·an [kŭs·tō′dē·ən] A guard or keeper: The students liked to help the *custodian*.

cy·clone [sī′klōn] A violent windstorm: We stayed in the cellar during the *cyclone*.

D d

deaf [dĕf] **deaf·ness** Completely or partially unable to hear: *Deafness* may be the result of an illness.

de·ci·sion [dĭ·sĭzh′ən] The making up of one's mind: He said his *decision* was final.

deck-chair [dĕk·châr] A lightweight folding chair: I placed my *deck-chair* in the sun.

dec·o·rate [dĕk′ə·rāt] To make fancy or pretty: They bought new wallpaper to *decorate* the house.

ded·i·cate [dĕd·ə·kāt] **ded·i·cat·ed** To set apart for a special purpose: The scientist *dedicated* her life to find a cure for measles.

de·prive [dĭ·prīv′] To take away from: We do not want to *deprive* you of your rest.

depth [dĕpth] Distance to the bottom or to the back: The *depth* of the pool was eight feet.

dig·ni·fied [dĭg′nə·fīd] Having dignity; proud: He walked in a *dignified* manner.

dis·gust [dĭs·gŭst′] **dis·gust·ed** Filled with intense dislike: His sloppy manners *disgusted* his friends.

dis·turb [dĭs·tûrb′] **dis·turb·ing** 1. To worry, upset. 2. To bother: The thunder was *disturbing* the animals' sleep.

doub·le [dŭb′əl] 1. In baseball, a hit that enables the player to get to second base. 2. Twice as much: He wanted a *double* portion of dessert.

draw·ing-room [drô′ĭng rōōm] A room in which visitors are entertained: The guests had coffee served to them in the *drawing-room*.

dune [d(y)ōōn] **dunes** A hill of loose sand: We stood on the sand *dune*.

dye [dī] **dyes** 1. To give lasting color by soaking in a liquid. 2. A colored preparation: Beautiful *dyes* to color cloth are made from plants.

E e

e·lec·tron [ĭ·lĕk′trŏn] **e·lec·trons** Negatively charged particles that surround the central core of an atom: There are eight *electrons* in one atom of oxygen.

el·e·ment [ĕl′ə·mənt] Any of a number of substances of which all matter is made: Gold is an *element* found in rocks.

em·er·ald [ĕm·ər·əld] 1. A bright-green precious stone. 2. A bright-green color: My skirt is an *emerald* color.

en·dure [ĭn·d(y)ōōr] To put up with; tolerate: Doctors must *endure* long working days.

en·er·get·ic [ĕn′ər·jĕt′ĭk] Full of energy: Sue felt very *energetic* this morning and hopped right out of bed.

en·thu·si·asm [ĭn·thoō′zē·ăz′əm] A deep interest or liking: His *enthusiasm* for stamp collecting was seen in the large number of stamps he had.

eu·ca·lyp·tus [yoō′kə·lĭp′təs] An evergreen tree that is valuable for its oil and wood: *Eucalyptus* oil is used in some medicines for colds.

ex·hi·bi·tion [ĕk′sə·bĭsh′ən] A public show, as of art: We attended the local art *exhibition*.

F f

fail·ure [fāl′yər] 1. An unsuccessful attempt. 2. A person or thing that has failed: Joe was disappointed over the team's *failure* to win the game.

fake [fāk] Something or someone passed off as real; false: It can be difficult to tell whether diamonds are real or *fake*.

fa·vor [fā′vər] A kind act or service: She went to the store as a *favor* to me.

fer·ry [fĕr′ē] A boat to carry people, cars, or goods across a river or other body of water: We took a *ferry* to the island.

fig·ure skat·er [fĭg′yər skāt′ər] One who skates by tracing elaborate figures on ice: It takes many years of practice to be a good *figure skater*.

fire·man [fīr′mən] A person who tends the fire in a steam engine's furnace on a train: Jack enjoyed being a *fireman* on the old train.

flat·ter·er [flăt′ər·ər] **flat·ter·ers** One who praises insincerely: No one likes to receive praise from a *flatterer*.

flint [flĭnt] A hard, dark stone which produces sparks when struck against stone: The walls of the house were made of *flint*.

fly [flī] **flies** 1. To move through the air with wings. 2. In baseball, a ball batted high over the field: The center fielder caught all the *flies* that came his way.

foam [fōm] A white mass of small bubbles: The *foam* on the soda pop tickled his nose.

freight [frāt] Goods that are sent by train, plane, truck, or ship: The *freight* we are waiting for was sent by train.

fric·as·see [frĭk′ə·sē′] Meat that has been stewed and served with gravy: The chicken *fricassee* smelled delicious.

fun·nel [fŭn′əl] A whirling wind in a tornado: We could see the *funnel* of the tornado dip closer to the ground.

fu·ri·ous [fyŏŏr′ē·əs] Very angry: Dad was *furious* when someone ran into his car.

fuse [fyōōz] A metal device used in an electric circuit to prevent fire: We had to replace a *fuse* after the light went out.

G g

gen·er·a·tor [jĕn′ə·rā′tər] A machine that changes mechanical energy to electricity: We saw giant *generators* at the power plant.

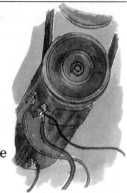

gift·ed [gĭf′tĭd] Talented: She is *gifted* with a great musical talent.

glide [glīd] **glid·ed** To move smoothly: He stopped skating with an easy *glide* to the side.

gold-rush [gōld rŭsh] The large migration of people to an area where gold has been discovered: Many people settled in California during the *gold-rush* days.

grace·ful [grās′fəl] Having or showing beauty of movement or behavior: Alice is a *graceful* dancer.

grant [grănt] To give: The king will *grant* you permission to leave.

grid [grĭd] An arrangement of lines that divides an area into small squares: Draw the *grid* lines one-quarter inch apart.

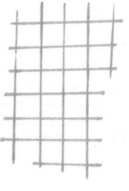

groom | **jagged**

groom [grōōm] **groomed** To attend to the feeding, cleaning, and brushing of a horse: The owner of the horse *groomed* him carefully.

H h

hand·i·craft [hăn′dē·krăft′] **hand·i·crafts** A skill in which the hands are used: A *handicraft* like woodworking can be profitable as well as fun.

hes·i·tate [hĕz′ə·tāt] **hes·i·tat·ed** To pause before acting: She *hesitated* before answering the question.

hitch [hĭch] **hitched** To fasten or to tie: The cowhand *hitched* his horse to the fence.

hock·ey [hŏk′ē] A game played on ice in which players try to drive a puck into the goal: It takes much skill to play ice *hockey*.

home·land [hōm′lănd′] The country that is usually one's place of birth: It had been a long time since he saw his *homeland*.

home·stead [hōm′stĕd] A piece of land and a home: She longed to return to the old *homestead*.

hur·ri·cane [hûr′ə·kān] A storm with very heavy rains and high winds: A *hurricane* often begins in the West Indies.

hur·tle [hûr′təl] **hur·tled** To move along with great speed: The boulder *hurtled* down the mountainside.

I i

im·pa·tient [ĭm·pā′shənt] Easily annoyed; having no patience: Jack was *impatient* with Bob's slowness.

in·com·pa·ra·ble [ĭn·kŏm′pər·ə·bəl] It that can't be equaled or compared: His desire to learn was *incomparable* to anything I'd seen.

in·dig·nant [ĭn·dĭg′nənt] **in·dig·nant·ly** Angry because something is not right or fair: The batter stared *indignantly* at the umpire at the call "Strike three!"

in·ter·rupt [ĭn′tə·rŭpt′] **in·ter·rupt·ed** To cause a person to stop speaking or working by breaking in; to get in the way: My dinner was *interrupted* by a telephone call.

is·land [ī′lənd] Land surrounded by water: Hawaii is a large *island* in the Pacific Ocean.

J j

jag·ged [jăg′ĭd] An uneven edge that has sharp points: The broken glass has a *jagged* edge.

337

jave·lin
[jăv′(ə)lĭn] A light spear once used as a weapon, but now thrown for distance in athletic contests: Tom throws the *javelin* for our school's track team.

L l

lab·o·ra·to·ry [lăb′rə·tôr′ē] A place equipped for doing scientific work: My brother works in the hospital *laboratory*.

lace [lās] 1. To fasten together with a lace or laces. 2. To twist together or intertwine: Let me *lace* your shoes for you.

la·goon [lə·gōōn′] A body of water that is shallow: There were two beautiful swans in the *lagoon*.

lan·tern [lăn′tərn] A case with sides of glass or paper to hold and protect a light: In the early days before electricity, you might use a *lantern* for light.

league [lēg] A group of athletic teams that usually compete among themselves: Their baseball team had the highest score in the *league*.

leg·end [lĕj′ənd] A story that has come down from earlier times: The story of Hiawatha is a favorite *legend*.

lo·cate [lō′kāt] To find: He could not *locate* the house with the address he was given.

loom [lōōm] **looms** A machine on which thread is woven into cloth: Beautiful rugs can be woven on *looms*.

lope [lōp] **loped** To run with a steady stride: The dog *loped* easily beside his master.

lop-eared [lŏp′ĭrd] Drooping ears: A beagle is a *lop-eared* dog.

lush [lŭsh] Full of a healthy growth of trees and plants; growing well: The *lush* tree produced much fruit.

M m

mad·man [măd′măn′] A person who is mad: They all thought Columbus was a *madman* when he said the world was round.

ma·te·ri·al [mə·tîr′ē·əl] **ma·te·ri·als** The substance of which a thing is made: What *material* did she use for her coat?

mead·ow [mĕd′ō] A piece of land where grass is grown for hay or for grazing: We saw a family of deer grazing in the *meadow*.

mes·sage [mĕs′ĭj] **mes·sages** News, advice, or other communication sent to another person: Did you see the *message* I left by the phone?

mim·e·o·graph [mĭm′ē·ə·grăf′] **mim·e·o·graphed** To use a machine that prints copies from a stencil: The teacher *mimeographed* copies of the pupils' papers.

mis·er·a·ble [mĭz′ər·ə·bəl] Very unhappy: The girl who lost the race felt *miserable*.

mount [mount] To get up on: You must learn the proper way to *mount* a horse.

mur·mur [mûr′mər] **mur·mured** A low, unclear, and steady sound: The *murmur* of the crowd quieted when she began to sing.

mus·lin [mŭz′lĭn] A strong cotton cloth: The dresses were made of plain *muslin*.

N n

na·tion·al [năsh′ən·əl] Belonging to a whole nation: The *national* flag is a symbol of a country.

nour·ish [nûr′ĭsh] **nour·ished, nour·ish·ing** To keep alive and healthy or help to grow with food: To be strong, people must eat *nourishing* food.

nug·get [nŭg′ĭt] **nug·gets** A lump of gold in its natural state: She found two tiny *nuggets* in the pan of sand.

O o

old-fash·ioned [ōld′ făsh′ənd] Out of fashion or date: The *old-fashioned* stagecoach led the parade.

old mas·ter [ōld măs′tər] One of the great European painters before the 18th century: Rembrandt is a well-known *old master*.

op·er·a·tion [ŏp′ə·rā′shən] An act performed on the body, usually with instruments, to cure or repair an illness or injury: Rick's *operation* on his broken leg was successful.

o·pin·ion [ə·pĭn′yən] A judgment of the excellence or value of a person or thing: What is your *opinion* of this necklace?

o·ver·load [ō′vər·lōd] To put heavy or too great a load on something: Using too many appliances at the same time will *overload* the circuits.

o·ver·whelm [ō′vər·(h)wĕlm′]
o·ver·whelmed To overcome
completely; overpower or crush, as
with force or feeling: My sister
was *overwhelmed* with joy when
she received her college diploma.

ox [ŏks] A bull
used as a work
animal: The old
ox pulled the
heavy plow.

P p

pal·ette [păl′ĭt] A
board used by
artists for
mixing paints:
The artist
cleaned his
palette carefully
before adding the
new paints.

pe·cul·iar [pĭ·kyōōl′yər] Different
or strange: There are many
peculiar fish in the sea.

per·sua·sion [pər·swā′zhən] The
ability to induce one to believe or
do something: Mary used gentle
persuasion to get Jane to go with
her.

pho·no·graph
[fō′nə·grăf] A
device that
reproduces sound
from grooves in a
record: Father
said we must be
careful when we
play the
phonograph.

pho·to·cop·y [fō′tō·kŏp′ē] A copy or
reproduction made by a machine
of printed material: I have filed
the *photocopy* of the story in my
drawer.

plat·form
[plăt′fôrm] A
raised flat
surface: Six
people stood on
the *platform*
waiting for the
train.

plunge [plŭnj] A jump or a dive:
He was ready to *plunge* into the
cool water.

Po·land [pō′lənd] A country in
North Central Europe: Do you
know anyone who lives in *Poland*?

pot·ter·y
[pŏt′ər·ē] Vases,
pots and other
things molded
from clay: She
gave me a piece
of *pottery* she
had made.

pre·cious [prĕsh′əs] Highly prized; valuable: My mother's ring is *precious* to me.

pres·ent [prez′ənt] A gift: Jane brought Andy a birthday *present*.

prompt [prŏmpt] **prompt·ly** Quickly; on time: Be there *promptly* at eight o'clock.

pub·lish [pŭb′lĭsh] **pub·lish·ing** To print and issue books, newspapers, and magazines for sale: The editor was against *publishing* the article.

puz·zle [pŭz′əl] **puz·zled** Confused or perplexed: Pete was *puzzled* about the oddly shaped box and what it might contain.

Q q

quill [kwĭl] **quills** 1. A large sharp spine. 2. A large feather from the wing or tail of a bird: The young boy looked for long *quills* after the birds left the park.

R r

ra·di·um [rā′dē·əm] A radioactive element found in ores of uranium: *Radium* salts are sometimes used in medical treatment.

re·ap·proach [rē′ə·prōch′] **re·ap·proached** To come nearer in space and time again: We *reapproached* the door to the office.

reed [rēd] **reeds** Any grass having a hollow stem: The turtle was hiding in the *reeds* along the river bank.

rein [rān] **reins** Straps attached to the bit to control an animal: Alice pulled on the *reins* to stop the horse.

re·lieve [rĭ·lēv′] **re·lieved** To lessen or ease: Her fears were *relieved* when she saw he was already home.

re·tire [rĭ·tīr′] **re·tired, re·tir·ing** 1. To go to bed. 2. To withdraw from a job: She plans on *retiring* next year.

re·tir·ing [rĭ·tīr′ing] Shy; modest: He was *retiring* in his manner.

road·bed [rōd′bĕd′] The foundation on which railroad tracks are laid: They hurried to repair the *roadbed* before the train was due to pass over it.

road·mas·ter [rōd′măs′tər] A railroad maintenance official: The *roadmaster* shouted orders to the crew.

ru·in [rōō′ĭn] **ru·ined** To destroy, demolish, or damage: Joe watched sadly as the waves *ruined* his sand castle.

rule [rōōl] To have authority or control over; govern: We must elect a president to *rule* over the meetings.

run·ner [rŭn′ər] **run·ners** The part of an object on which it slides: My skates need new *runners*.

S s

sat·is·fy [săt′ĭs·fī] **sat·is·fied** Being supplied with what is needed or wanted: Have you eaten enough to feel *satisfied*?

sched·ule [skĕj′ōōl] 1. An agreed upon time. 2. A plan for how things are to be done: Did you see the *schedule* for this week's work?

scud [skŭd] **scud·ded** To move, run, or fly quickly: Dark clouds *scudded* across the sky and hid the sun.

seek [sēk] To look for; to go in search of: The young woman left home to *seek* work in another city.

shaft [shăft] One of two poles by which an animal is harnessed to a wagon: We made a new *shaft* to replace the broken one so that we could continue our journey by wagon.

shiv·er [shĭv′ər] **shiv·er·ing** To tremble or shake as though cold: Ben began *shivering* when he felt the cold air.

shoot [shōōt] **shoots** A young bud or plant: The children waited patiently for the new *shoots* to grow into mature plants.

shriek [shrēk] **shriek·ing** Sharp, shrill screaming: My brother began *shrieking* when he saw the snake.

sign [sīn] **signed** To communicate by using signals: I *signed* to my friend to come toward me.

sil·ver·ware [sĭl′vər·wâr′] Table utensils made of silver: Please polish the *silverware* before you set the table.

sin·gle [sĭng′gəl] **sin·gles** 1. A person alone; an individual. 2. In baseball, a hit that enables one to get to first base: He hoped he could hit a *single*.

snatch [snăch] **snatched** To grab hold of suddenly: The duck *snatched* the bread from my fingers.

soc·cer [sŏk′ər] A game in which the ball can be kicked or struck with any part of the body except the hands: *Soccer* is a popular game in England.

sol·emn [sŏl′əm] Serious, grave and earnest: The silence in the room was *solemn*.

Span·iards [spăn′yərdz] People from Spain: The *Spaniards* came to America for vacation.

spec·ta·tor [spĕk′tā·tər] **spec·ta·tors** A person who watches an event: The *spectator* yelled loudly in her excitement during the football game.

sput·ter [spŭt′ər] **sput·tered** To make a hissing or spitting sound: The old car rattled, *sputtered*, and then broke down.

stir·rup [stûr′əp] A loop that is connected to a saddle by a strap which holds a horse rider's foot: The girl kept her foot in the *stirrup* as she rode the horse.

storm cel·lar [stôrm′ sĕl′ər] An underground shelter used during violent storms: They kept food, water, a cot, and a radio in the *storm cellar*.

stow [stō] **stowed, stow·ing** To pack in a neat, close way: The people are *stowing* their belongings in a safe place.

stroke [strōk] **stroked** To gently pet an animal: The child *stroked* the wet fur of the dog.

strug·gle [strŭg′əl] A violent effort: Both teams will *struggle* to win the game of tug of war.

sub·ject [sŭb′jĭkt] The person, thing, or idea which is being spoken about: What was the *subject* they were discussing?

sup·pose [sə·pōz′] To assume as true; to imagine or guess: I *suppose* the bus will arrive on time.

syl·la·bar·y [sĭl′ə·bâr′ē] A set of written symbols, each of which represents a syllable: The Cherokee language is written by using a *syllabary*.

sym·bol [sĭm′bəl] **sym·bols** A mark or sign used to stand for something, as a plus sign: A rancher brands the cattle with the *symbol* of the ranch.

T t

taught [tôt] The past tense of *teach*: I *taught* my brother how to read.

te·di·ous [tē′dē·əs] Dull and tiresome: Jack thought painting the fence would be a *tedious* job.

tel·e·type·writ·er [těl′ə·tīp′rī′tər] A telegraph on which a message is sent from a typewriter-like keyboard, and which is automatically typed out at its destination: We sent the information on the *teletypewriter*.

the·a·tre [thē′ə·tər] A place built for presentations of films and plays: We went to the *theatre* to see the play.

throne [thrōn] The raised ornamental seat used by a ruler or king: The king's *throne* was decorated with gold and jewels.

to·tem pole [tō′təm pō′l] **to·tem poles** A tall pole carved or painted with symbols by North American Indians: The young brave was proud of the *totem pole* in his village.

trav·el·er [trăv′əl·ər] One who goes from place to place: The weary *traveler* was glad to get home again.

tre·men·dous [trĭ·měn′dəs] 1. Dreadful; awful. 2. Enormous: A *tremendous* clap of thunder made everyone jump.

trudge [trŭj] **trudged** To walk wearily as if with great effort: The little child *trudged* slowly behind his mother.

twist·er [twĭs′tər] A person or thing that turns or revolves: A tornado is sometimes called a *twister*.

U u

un·count·ed [ŭn·koun′tĭd] **un·count·a·ble** Not counted; too many to count: The number of light bulbs in America are *uncountable*.

u·nit·ed [yo͞o·nī′tĭd] Combined into one or joined together: We are *united* in our decision to travel on.

un·u·su·al [un·yo͞o′zho͞o·əl] Not ordinary; uncommon: It was *unusual* for the teacher to be late.

V v

valve [vălv] A device that controls the flow of a fluid: The faucet dripped because the *valve* was broken.

ve·ran·da
[və·răn′də] A long, open porch along the outside of a building: The young people liked to sit on the *veranda*.

vi·bra·tion [vī·brā′shən] **vi·bra·tions**
A rapid motion from side to side: An earthquake causes *vibrations* for many miles.

W w

wa·ver [wā′vər] **wa·vered** To show signs of falling back or giving way; falter: He *wavered* from his decision to leave and stayed at the party.

wealth·y [wĕl′thē] Being rich: Many people would like to be *wealthy*.

weight [wāt] The heaviness of a thing: John stood on the scales to check his *weight*.

whim·per [(h)wĭm′pər]
A low, sad, broken cry: The frightened puppy will *whimper* in the rain.

whirl [(h)wûrl] **whirl·ing** To go around or spin very fast: Dry leaves were *whirling* in the wind.

whisk [(h)wĭsk]
A small wire instrument used for whipping: Mother used a *whisk* to scramble the eggs.

wick·ed [wĭk′ĭd] Evil: The *wicked* witch tried to stop Dorothy.

wid·ow [wĭd′ō] A woman who has lost her husband through death: The woman had been a *widow* for five years.

width [wĭdth] Size, as measured from one side to another: The *width* of the desk is three feet.

win·dow box
[wĭn′dō bŏks′] A long narrow box on or outside a window ledge: Bright red flowers were growing in the *window box*.

wire·less [wīr′lĭs] A telegram sent by radio: I must send a *wireless* to the captain today.

with·er [wĭth′ər] To become dry and lifeless: Plants will *wither* and die without water.

wring [rĭng] To squeeze or twist: *Wring* the water out of your swim suit and hang it up to dry.

X x

x-ray [ĕks′rā] **x-rays**
Electromagnetic waves that have
great penetrating power: The
doctor looked at the *x-rays* of the
patient's broken arm.

Y y

yield [yēld] **yielded** To give forth;
produce: Our garden *yielded* many
vegetables this year.

ACKNOWLEDGMENTS

For permission to adapt and reprint copyrighted materials, grateful acknowledgment is made to the following publishers, authors, and other copyright holders:

Eleanor Cameron, author, for "Janey by Moonlight." Copyright ©1983 by Eleanor Cameron. Used by permission of the author.

Patricia Edwards Clyne, author, for "Hi-Me." Used by permission of the author.

Amelia Burr Elmore's family, executors, for "Rain in the Night" from *Life and Living* by Amelia Josephine Burr (Elmore). Reprinted by permission of Amelia Burr Elmore's family.

Harper & Row, Publishers, Inc., for "Summer Snow" from *All That Sunlight* by Charlotte Zolotow, copyright ©1967 by Charlotte Zolotow; and for "Snowy Benches" from *Out in the Dark and Daylight* by Aileen Fisher, copyright ©1980 by Aileen Fisher, both by permission of Harper & Row, Publishers, Inc.

William H. Hooks, author, for "Maria's Cave" adapted from *Maria's Cave* by William H. Hooks. Copyright ©1977 by William H. Hooks. Used by permission of the author.

Houghton Mifflin Company, for "A Song of Greatness" from *The Children Sing in the Far West* by Mary Austin, copyright 1928 by Mary Austin, copyright renewed 1956 by Kenneth M. Chapman and Mary C. Wheelwright, reprinted by permission of Houghton Mifflin Company; for "Lost in the Storm" from *Lost in the Storm* by Carol Carrick, copyright ©1974 by Carol and Donald Carrick, reprinted by permission of Ticknor & Fields/Clarion Books, A Houghton Mifflin Company; for "A Bear Called Paddington" from *A Bear Called Paddington* by Michael Bond, illustrated by Peggy Fortnum, copyright ©1958 by Michael Bond, reprinted by permission of Houghton Mifflin Company; and for "The Fast Sooner Hound" from *The Fast Sooner Hound* by Arna Bontemps, copyright ©1942 by Arna Bontemps and Jack Conroy, reprinted by permission of Houghton Mifflin Company.

Barbara Huff, author, for "The Library" from *Favorite Poems Old and New* selected by Helen Ferris, Doubleday & Company, 1957. Reprinted by permission of the author.

McGraw-Hill Publishing Company, for "The Golden Touch" by Nathaniel Hawthorne. ©1959 by Paul Galdone. Used by permission of the publisher.

Macmillan Publishing Co., Inc., for "The Coin" from *Collected Poems* by Sara Teasdale. Copyright 1920 by Macmillan Publishing Co., Inc., renewed 1948 by Mamie T. Wheless. Reprinted with permission of Macmillan Publishing Company.

Eve Merriam, author, for "Associations" from *There Is No Rhyme for Silver* by Eve Merriam. Copyright ©1962 by Eve Merriam. Reprinted by permission of the author.

Modern Curriculum Press, for "Motor Cars" from *Songs around a Toadstool Table* by Rowena Bastin Bennett. Copyright ©1967 by Rowena Bastin Bennett. Used by permission of Modern Curriculum Press.

Harold Ober Associates, Inc., for "City" from *Golden Slippers* by Langston Hughes. Copyright 1941 by Harper & Row, Publishers, Inc. Reprinted by permission of Harold Ober Associates, Inc.

Mary L. O'Neill, author, for "Memory" from *Words, Words, Words* by Mary L. O'Neill. Reprinted by permission of the author.

Random House, Inc., for "The Skates of Uncle Richard" adapted by permission of Random House, Inc., from *The Skates of Uncle Richard* by Carol Fenner. Copyright ©1978 by Carol Fenner Williams.

The Saturday Evening Post Company, for "The Horse Who Went Fishing" by Jean Morris from *Jack and Jill* magazine, copyright ©1973 by The Saturday Evening Post Company, Indianapolis, Indiana; for "Where the Bear Went over the Mountain" by Blaine G. Goodman from *Child Life* magazine, copyright ©1973 by The Saturday Evening Post Company, Indianapolis, Indiana; and for "Home-Run Hannibal" by Robert D. Culp from *Young World* magazine, copyright ©1977 by The Saturday Evening Post Company, Indianapolis, Indiana, all adapted by permission of the publisher.

347

Charles Scribner's Sons, for "The Rooster Who Understood Japanese" by Yoshiko Uchida, adapted from *The Rooster Who Understood Japanese*. Text copyright ©1976 Yoshiko Uchida. Used by permission of Charles Scribner's Sons.

Vanguard Press, Inc., for "Pettranella" from *Pettranella* by Betty Waterton. Copyright ©1980 by Betty Waterton. Reprinted by permission of Vanguard Press, Inc., and Douglas and McIntyre, Canada.

Western Publishing Company, for "Open Range" by Kathryn and Byron Jackson from *Tenggren's Cowboys and Indians*, ©1968, 1948 by Western Publishing Company, Inc. Reprinted by permission.

Albert Whitman & Company, for "Words in Our Hands" by Ada B. Litchfield, adapted from *Words in Our Hands*, text ©1980 by Ada B. Litchfield. Reprinted with the permission of Albert Whitman & Company.

Grateful acknowledgment is made to the following for illustrations, photographs, and reproductions on the pages indicated:

Edward Arnold 214-215; John M. Beals 232-235; The Bettmann Archive 154-155, 157-159, 161; Donald Carrick 134-137, 139-140, 142, 144-147, 149; Randy Chewning 252-254, 256-258, 260-263; Floyd Cooper 152, 222, 224-225, 227-230; Jim Cummins 194, 196, 198, 201, 203; Dr. E. R. Degginger 308 (top); Linda Edwards 116-119, 121-122, 125; C. S. Ewing 204-207, 209-210, 213; Elizabeth Fong 12-13, 15, 17-18, 20-26, 28, 30-33; Peggy Fortnum 314, 316, 318, 320, 323, 325; Four By Five Southwest 54-55, 90, 128, 130-131; David R. Frazier 308 (bottom), 310; Jon Goodell 150-151; Connie Hwang 231; Dennis Jones 44, 66, 84, 110, 132, 162, 192, 216, 244, 266, 312, 326; Murray McKeehan 168-170, 172-173, 175-176, 179; Diana Magnuson 34, 36-38, 40-43; William Mathison title page, copyright page, 251; Y. Momatiuk/Amwest Picture Agency 129; Courtesy of Museum of the American Indian, Heye Foundation, New York 78-82; Tom Newsom 72, 75-77, 237, 239-240, 243; Brian Parker/Tom Stack & Associates 108; Betty Frank Plumlee 264; Vera Rosenberry 56-65, 86-89; Cratie Sandlin/Amwest Picture Agency 305; Bill Shires 10-11, 70-71, 114-115, 166-167, 220-221, 270-271; James N. Skeen/Nature Images Southeast 309; Philip Smith 46-47, 49-53, 180, 182-184, 186, 188-189, 191, 272, 274, 276-279, 281, 283-286, 289, 291-294, 296, 298-299, 301-303; John Spragens, Jr./Picture Group 304; Guy Tilden 83, 127, 233, 246, 248-250, 306-307; Mike Wimmer 68-69; Marsha Winborn 92, 95, 97-102, 104-105, 107.

The glossary illustrations are by Larry Simmons.